Books by Allan W. Eckert

* * *

THE GREAT AUK

A TIME OF TERROR

A
TIME
OF
TERROR

A
TIME
OF
TERROR

The Great Dayton Flood

by ALLAN W. ECKERT

with illustrations

LITTLE, BROWN AND COMPANY · BOSTON · TORONTO

Published simultaneously in Canada
by Little, Brown & Company (Canada) Limited

PRINTED IN THE UNITED STATES OF AMERICA

To
BILL FRANCOIS
for his aid, advice and
companionship through many
years — commodities never
abundant for any writer

Author's Note

THE CHARACTERS in this book are real people and the events and incidents in which they were involved actually happened. While much of the dialog that has been used here is verbatim, there are cases where, for the purpose of continuity and smoother reading, dialog has been created. In all such cases every effort has been made to do this in a manner entirely in character with the individual speaking and in keeping with the chain of events as they occurred.

It would be impractical here to attempt to acknowledge individually the large number of persons who — through personal interviews, diaries, telephone conversations, logbooks and various records — have helped supply me with the essential data, personal experience stories, eyewitness accounts and color that went into the preparation of this book. Their interest and assistance in this behalf are greatly appreciated.

Special acknowledgment, however, is made to: the Dayton *Journal Herald* and the Dayton *Daily News* for the wealth of material made available in their files; the Miami Conservancy District for its help not only in clarifying an infinite variety of details, but for the maps and charts which brought the subject into clear focus; the National Cash Register Company for its extensive aid in supplying records of its participation as the most important rescue and relief agency at the time, as well as for the photographs which accompany this book; and to Elizabeth Faries of the Dayton and Montgomery County Public Library, without whose cheerful and extended assistance the researching of materials for this book would have been a task considerably more difficult.

ALLAN W. ECKERT

Dayton, Ohio
May 1964

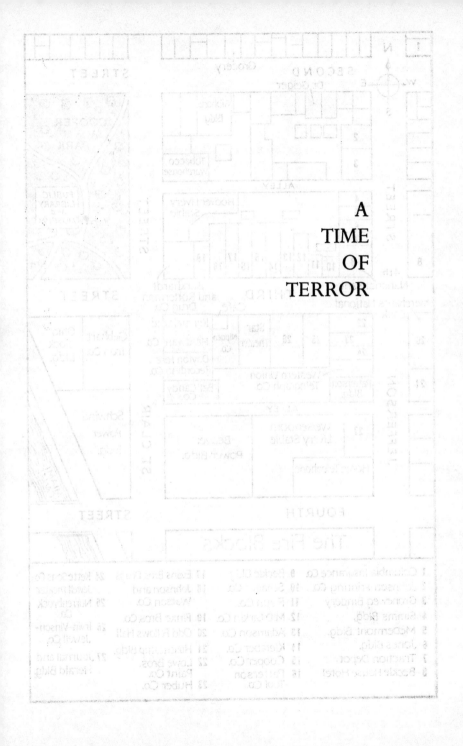

A
TIME
OF
TERROR

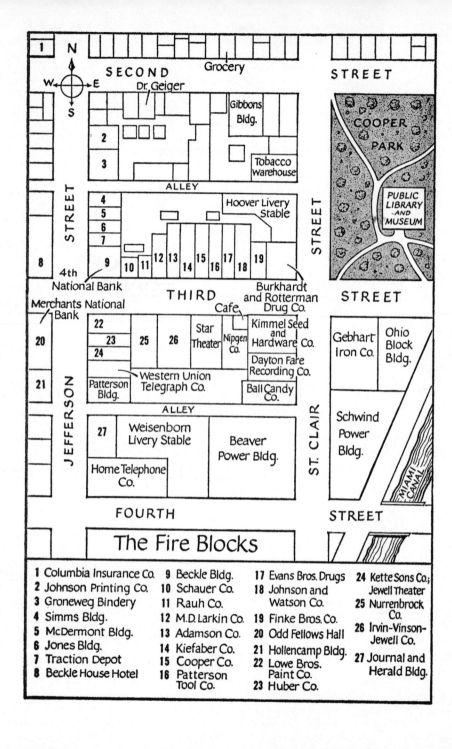

The Fire Blocks

1 Columbia Insurance Co.
2 Johnson Printing Co.
3 Groneweg Bindery
4 Simms Bldg.
5 McDermont Bldg.
6 Jones Bldg.
7 Traction Depot
8 Beckle House Hotel
9 Beckle Bldg.
10 Schauer Co.
11 Rauh Co.
12 M.D. Larkin Co.
13 Adamson Co.
14 Kiefaber Co.
15 Cooper Co.
16 Patterson Tool Co.
17 Evans Bros. Drugs
18 Johnson and Watson Co.
19 Finke Bros. Co.
20 Odd Fellows Hall
21 Hollencamp Bldg.
22 Lowe Bros. Paint Co.
23 Huber Co.
24 Kette Sons Co.; Jewell Theater
25 Nurrenbrock Co.
26 Irvin-Vinson-Jewell Co.
27 Journal and Herald Bldg.

Introduction

IN MID-MARCH of 1913 the stage was set for tragedy in Dayton, Ohio, and the preliminaries began with the development of three great air masses, each a thousand miles or more distant from the other two.

The first was an eddy of wind spawned in the tropical air of the Gulf of Mexico. It grew into a stiff warm wind which headed northward, crossing the Florida coastline at Panama City and Tallahassee and then sliding easily across Georgia, bringing summerlike weather to Atlanta. Its speed increased as it funneled through the Cumberland Gap and brought unseasonably warm temperatures to Lexington and Frankfort, Kentucky. It raced across the Ohio River at Cincinnati and then sped northward toward Dayton.

Another eddy began in the mouth of the St. Lawrence River, drifted slowly toward Quebec as it swiftly grew to gale proportions and then hurled itself southward past Montreal and Ottawa and Toronto. It was an icy blast of frigid Canadian air when it howled through Detroit, and at Toledo the temperature plummeted. It then headed due southward toward Dayton.

The third eddy formed in the northern Great Plains and quickly became a wind of hurricane force in central Nebraska, ripping and tearing a great swath through the dormant fields. It struck Omaha on Easter Sunday and dealt the city a devastating blow, leaving thousands homeless and hundreds injured, a few dead. As if satisfied with this venting of its wrath, it lost some of its strength and became only a gusty weather front filled with angry clouds, the frightful flash of lightning and tortured rumblings of thunder as it passed Des Moines and roared across Illinois, buffeting Peoria and Springfield, then increasing in vigor again as it neared Indianapolis. It paused there momentarily, gathered its resources for the contest ahead and then moved due eastward toward Dayton.

These three great air masses collided over a wide expanse of farmland, and their battleground extended almost to Indianapolis in the west, Fort Wayne and Lima in the north, Columbus to the east and, at the southern edge, Dayton.

In the 2500 square miles of ground over which this contest of the elements was being staged, a saturation point had already been reached. There had been a general thawing, and the ice and snows of a hard winter had melted and seeped into the ground. On top of this, several light rains had fallen, until now, in the third week of March, no more moisture could be absorbed into the ground and the water had to run off into the multitudes of ditches and creek beds throughout the countryside.

The rainfall to the west of Dayton eventually became

part of the inconsistent stream called Wolf Creek. In the northwest, the runoff went into the numerous tributaries of the normally serene and beautiful Stillwater River, which then carried it away to the south. In the north a multitude of creeks picked up the runoff and channeled it into the sprawling Great Miami River, one of the largest in the state. And in the northeast, the temperamental Mad River carried away excess precipitation.

These four streams had a common destination. Within less than one mile, all four converged inside the city limits of Dayton, a city of 130,000. There was a tragic peculiarity, however, in the geography of this sprawling industrial metropolis. Just after entering the city, the Great Miami River was joined by the Stillwater, and here the channel bed between levees was eight hundred feet wide. About a quarter of a mile downstream, at the eastern edge of the downtown business district, the Mad River joined the larger stream at a sharp bend, but here the channel was only seven hundred feet wide. Less than a half mile downstream the great river was joined by Wolf Creek, and here the levees were just six hundred feet apart. Finally, where the Great Miami passed the city limits to the south — now a much larger river than when it had entered — it flowed in a channel only five hundred feet wide.

It was as if, in some perversity of humor, man and nature had conspired to make Dayton's river system upside down; three hundred feet narrower where it left the city than where it entered. To further compound the hazard of such an arrangement, the converging rivers formed a great S-curve, with the treacherous base of that S rimming the downtown area.

Hindsight can make experts of even the most obtuse, but it is nevertheless astounding that so few people in the city seemed aware of its precarious position. It was almost unbelievably good fortune that devastating floods had not inundated the city regularly through the years. True, the lowlands surrounding it, as well as small low sectors within the city, often became flooded, but this was generally shrugged off as an unfortunate but unavoidable facet of life here.

The greater portion of the city, it was argued, was protected with fine earthen levees that could and would prevent serious flooding. In fact, even that tremendous downpour of 1866, which had swiftly sent the river up past flood level, had caused the only truly significant inundation in the city's history and then, due to these fine levees, the downtown area had been covered with only four feet of water for part of one day before it abated. No one could conceive of a harder rain than that hitting the Dayton area.

When those three great air masses collided, however, a sustained rainfall occurred which deposited an average of nearly nine inches of water on every foot of that 2500 square miles of territory. It amounted to a staggering total of three trillion, nine hundred twenty billion, four hundred million gallons of water. One has to make a comparison to appreciate just how much water that is. Niagara Falls, which discharges one million five hundred ninety thousand gallons of water *every second*, would have to take just short of twenty-eight full days to equal what fell here. This is enough water to fill a hole in the ground measuring twenty-five miles in length, a mile in width and twenty-five feet in depth!

Unable to be absorbed into the already saturated ground, this fantastic volume of water began following the pronounced slope of the land to the south, the run-off quickly growing from a trickle to a stream to a roaring wash and finally to a rampaging torrent in each of the four rivers.

These four great torrents, each traveling at approximately twenty-five miles per hour, met at 7 A.M. on March 25, 1913, inside the city limits of Dayton, Ohio.

It was a time of terror, and this is the story of what happened during that dreadful week.

Monday

✳ 11:30 A.M.

H ARRY ALPS of the United States Weather Bureau in Dayton finished his morning correlation of the weather data and then lit a cigarette. He settled back in the worn wooden desk chair and blew a cloud of blue-white smoke toward the ceiling, a small frown creasing his brow and a thoughtful look on his face.

The readings of the various gauges disturbed him because now the possibility of flooding, at least in the low-lying areas of the city, had become a probability. The river had risen more rapidly than he had expected and showed no early signs of cresting. He thought about the weekend just past and shook his head wryly. Saturday the river level at the Main Street bridge had stood at two feet and it had been such a beautifully sunny day he'd looked forward to a nice bright Easter Sunday. He tried to recall any Easter in the past when the weather had been really nice but couldn't think of one. This year's had been no exception.

[9]

Dawn on Sunday had broken with pouring rain and the entire day had been stormy. The wind was very gusty, sometimes even violent, and throughout the day the clouds had looked queer, not like Dayton's usual storm clouds. The rainfall had tapered off toward evening and by midnight had become only a fine drizzle with intermittent harder showers. But then, at five o'clock this morning, the heavens had opened and rain descended in great sheets, often so hard it was difficult to see across the street.

Several times during the morning the sky had brightened and the sun seemed on the verge of peeping through, but then the heavy black masses of odd-looking clouds would sweep across the sky shooting out jagged bolts of lightning and sounding an almost continual roll of thunder over the city. To Alps it had seemed colder out than the 58 degrees registered on the bureau's thermometer and he noted that the humidity was 100 per cent, meaning a saturated atmosphere and therefore no evaporation.

From 5 A.M. until now nearly an inch and a half of rain had fallen, and by 7 A.M. the river gauge had indicated seven feet. Since then it had risen steadily at almost a foot an hour until now it was 11.6 feet and higher than it had been at any time since early January.

Alps sighed and picked up his telephone. "George," he told his assistant, "looks like the lowlands are going to get it again. You and Harold start calling the residences in those areas to warn them. Be sure to let them know it isn't another case of *possible* flooding but that they'll be getting water in a few hours if they haven't already. I'll help you two with the calls after I contact Dodds."

He broke the connection and called Dayton's safety director, Mays Dodds, explained the situation and suggested he have the city employees set about shutting off the storm sewers and starting up the big electric pumps that kept the lowlands dry when the river level rose above them on the other side of the levee. Dodds listened carefully.

"How bad do you think it might get?" he asked when Alps finished.

"Depends a lot on whether or not this rain quits soon," Alps replied, adding, "not only here but to the north of us. We just got a report from Piqua and they've recorded 3.7 inches of rain already. That hasn't even reached us yet. Without any more rain we'll get a crest of fourteen feet or more anyway, so the low areas will definitely get lots of water. I have a crew calling the residents in those areas to warn 'em, but it might be a good idea to alert the police and fire departments in case the situation gets worse."

There was a short pause, and then Dodds asked, "Might it?"

"It could," Alps answered immediately.

"How much worse?"

"It might hit sixteen feet. Possibly more."

"Let's see," Dodds said slowly, "flood level is . . . what?"

"Eighteen feet."

"And if it went over that? What about the downtown area?"

"We'd probably have relatively serious flooding in some

of the residential areas and maybe a few inches on the downtown streets, but I don't think any more than that. Official flood stage is eighteen feet but the levees should be able to contain up to twenty-three feet."

Dodds sounded relieved. "I'll get my men on the job right away," he said. "And don't worry about the police and fire departments. I'll alert them. Is there any chance the flooding will get so bad we'll need the National Guard?"

"Oh, I doubt that," Alps said hastily. "Even if it should come to that, we've got plenty of time. I'll be sure to keep in touch with you — Mayor Phillips, too — and if it begins to look bad enough, I'll let you know right away, okay?"

"That's fine," Mays Dodds said. "Might be a good idea if I called the newspapers and advised them, too. They'll probably want to print a warning for the low areas."

* **4:15** P.M.
MONDAY

For the third time that afternoon, the president of the sprawling National Cash Register Company at the southern outskirts of Dayton walked to his ninth-floor office window and looked out over the city. A pall of industrial and residential smoke held low by the atmosphere made visibility poor, and the winding Miami River, greatly swollen now, reflected the dismal iron gray of the sky.

At sixty-eight, John H. Patterson was a rather slight,

impeccably dressed individual who wore small gold-rimmed eyeglasses and sported a fine thick moustache. The nation's foremost pioneer of industrial welfare, his was the iron hand that had founded the firm thirty years before with a modest $15,000 and molded it into the huge multimillion-dollar enterprise it was now. But on this afternoon he was plagued with serious thoughts not connected with the business of manufacturing cash registers.

The rain drummed monotonously on the windowsill and for a long while the industrialist stood there, hands clasped behind his back. Then he called to his secretary.

"Mr. Barringer, I want an umbrella. I'm going up to the roof."

John Barringer, long accustomed to highly unusual comments and requests from his employer, showed no surprise. He got the umbrella and accompanied Patterson to the top of the ten-story building. The two men walked over to the northwest corner high above South Main Street and looked silently out over the downtown area a mile and a half to the north.

Barringer had no idea what the matter was, but he knew that his employer was indeed troubled. Patterson cleared his throat several times and pursed his lips so that his moustache seemed to become a cushion for his nose. He also rubbed his right thumb over the fingertips of the same hand. Small indications they were to what the man was thinking, but important nonetheless. Barringer had seen Patterson use these same gestures individually on numerous occasions before important decisions were made. Rarely, however, had he seen all three made at once.

The four-thirty whistle blew and they watched as the several thousand men who worked here left for home, many of them living in the residential areas surrounding the plant.

"It's raining out," Patterson said, as if neither man had been aware of the fact until now. "It is also quitting time. Let's go home, Mr. Barringer."

✳ 4:45 P.M.
MONDAY

Harry Alps put down his telephone wearily and looked at the wall clock. There'd be no getting home on time tonight. He and his two staff members had already called over four hundred residents of the low-lying districts, warned them of the coming high water and asked them to pass the word to their neighbors, but the situation had become considerably worse since then and now new areas were threatened.

At noon the meteorologist had thought perhaps the river might crest as high as fourteen feet. Now he'd have to raise that estimate considerably. The downpour — as hard a rain as he'd ever seen — had continued all day, not only here but in all areas within a hundred miles of Dayton to the east, north and west. Precipitation records in most communities were being broken and runoff was reported as severe — and this runoff had not, for the most part, even reached Dayton yet. At 2 P.M. the river gauge showed twelve feet and while the last reading forty-five minutes ago had shown an increase of only four inches, it was obvious there'd be a big jump as soon as the runoff came in, which he estimated would be about midnight.

One of his men had to leave at 5 P.M., but the other agreed to stay on with Alps and continue making calls. The evening crew would be on hand shortly, and with all of them working at it, they should be able to get most of the residents warned. That is, Alps amended to himself, if this rain will quit soon. He didn't like to think of what would happen if it didn't.

He picked up his phone again and placed another call. "Hello, Mr. Dodds? This is Harry Alps here. It's beginning to look worse than we expected. If this rain doesn't stop pretty soon — which, quite frankly, doesn't look too likely at present — the river'll crest about flood stage. This thing could become pretty bad. I think it might be a good idea if, as you mentioned earlier, you were to alert the National Guard to stand by. We ought to know by midnight or shortly after what's going to happen."

✳ 5 P.M.
MONDAY

Dayton police chief John Allabeck spoke into the instrument to the department switchboard operator.

"I want you to call every off-duty officer," he said briskly. "Put them on stand-by notice. We've received word that the lowland will get some severe flooding and we may even get some high water in areas that don't

normally get it. I expect we'll be able to handle everything well enough with the on-duty men, but those on
stand-by are to stay in their homes during off-duty hours
until further notice, just in case. Clear?"

"Yes, sir."

Allabeck put down the phone and rang for his assistant. The officer entered almost immediately. "Bill," the
chief said, "I want every available on-duty man for
detail in the low sections of the city tonight. There's no
doubt there'll be some locally severe flooding in those
areas. Get your men out on a house-to-house in North
Dayton, the near West Side, Riverdale, lower Dayton
View and all other areas near the levees. Have them
warn all residents and advise them to leave for higher
ground immediately."

"Yes, sir."

Allabeck sighed deeply as the young officer left the
room. This flooding problem was perennial. Every year,
spring and fall, they had to warn the same people to
move to higher ground.

One of these days, he thought, I'm just going to
ignore the weather bureau's predictions and let 'em get
caught. Serve 'em right for staying in those areas just
as if they didn't know any better. Might even teach 'em
a lesson.

✳ 6 P.M.
MONDAY

Andrew M. Fox was met at the front door of his
house at 629 North Main Street by his wife, who smiled

somewhat lopsidedly. Her voice, when she greeted him, studiously skirted any hint of condescension or criticism.

"Well, how does it look, Andy?"

"Not good, Finette. Not good at all. There's going to be a bad flood. A very bad one. I may have to stay up all night tonight."

Finette Fox turned quickly away and went into the kitchen so he wouldn't see the exasperation she felt. Why, she wondered, did she have to have a husband who felt it was his duty to be the boy at the dike who saves the nation? Time after time in the years they'd been married he had done this — dutifully trudging the three blocks to the levee at Steele Dam, watching the water rise and then, when it reached a certain point, hustling from house to house warning people to move out, that a flood was coming. The first few times he had actually cleared the neighborhood, but when there had never been more than the most minor flooding, people began to call him High Water Fox and laugh at him behind his back.

He had been going to the levee every couple of hours since early morning today, and each time he returned home more certain that this time it was going to be the big one, the major flood he'd been announcing for years.

He scarcely looked at the food his wife set before him for dinner and chewed in a preoccupied manner. She knew he wouldn't even remember what it was he had eaten five minutes after he left the table, and she was right. A little needling anger touched her and for a moment she was on the verge of having it out with him — telling him he was just being silly, that he was a laughingstock of the neighborhood, that every time it rained he neglected both his coal business and his real estate dealings — to say nothing of his wife! — in favor of standing on the levee in the rain watching the water rise. Instead, she merely blew a wisp of hair out of her eyes and changed her mind. It wouldn't do any good, she knew. They'd just squabble back and forth for the better part of an hour or so and then he'd leave as he was going to anyway, to go back to that stupid levee.

Andrew Fox finished his dinner and walked to the window, where he stood silently watching the rain pelt into the street for a few minutes. Then he shrugged into his raincoat again and at the front door he turned to smile briefly at his wife.

"I think I'll go over to the levee and see how the river looks, Fin." He said it as if this were the first time he'd ever considered doing such a thing.

Finette Fox shook her head sadly as the door closed behind him.

Tuesday: 2:20 A.M.

EVEN THROUGH the fog of sleepiness that enveloped him, Mays Dodds could detect the deep concern in Harry Alps's voice coming through the telephone. The safety director asked few questions, listening carefully as the weatherman told him the bad news: the river gauge, which had hit fourteen feet at 8 P.M., fifteen at 10 P.M. and over sixteen at midnight, now showed eighteen feet eight inches with no cresting of the river in prospect. There was now, Alps warned, no doubt that the downtown area would get flooded by at least a foot or two of water, and the residential areas might get five or six feet.

Dodds thanked him, advised him to continue warning those residents he could reach by telephone and hung up. In quick succession he called the local National Guard commander, fire chief Ed Ramby and police chief John Allabeck, relaying to them what he had learned and asking each to send patrols into the areas sure to be flooded to begin evacuation.

✳ **3 A.M.**
TUESDAY

As soon as Finette Fox opened her eyes and saw her husband beside the bed with the lantern in his hand and still wearing the dripping raincoat, she knew it had happened again. The water in the Great Miami River had reached "that" point again where his observations took concrete action.

"Still coming up, Andy?" she asked sleepily, avoiding meeting his eyes.

Something in the tone of her voice, perhaps a shading of disbelief, made him look more closely at her, and he sat on the side of the bed, leaned over and kissed her gently on the nose.

"Honey," he said softly, "look at me."

She raised her eyes to his and saw that the look there was intense, that his brow was furrowed with genuine concern. She started to say something but he pressed a finger to her lips and shook his head.

"Listen first," he said. "I know I've warned about floods lots of times and" — the confession came hard — "mostly I've been wrong. People have laughed at me. I really don't care. But I do care what *you* think, Finette. This time there's no doubt about it. We're going to have a terrible flood. Maybe twenty–thirty feet deep. I've got the wagon ready out front. Get dressed and start gathering whatever you have that you can carry and want to save. We've got to get away and somehow convince the others around here what's happening."

"Come on, Harold," he said. "Milkin' time."

The fourteen-year-old turned his head into his pillow and gave another muffled moan, then sat up as the shaking became stronger and squinted his eyes against the glow of the lantern his father was holding.

"Feel like I just got to sleep, Pa. Ain't it earlier than usual?" He asked the question hopefully, but the gaunt-faced farmer shook his head and smiled.

"Quarter of five, same as always. Cows is bellerin' already. Reckon you'd sleep till noon if you could get away with it. How you ever gonna manage this farm when I ain't around no more?"

"Shucks, Pa," the boy grinned, "I reckon you'll always be around." He lifted the chimney on his own kerosene lamp and lit the wick. It smoked heavily for an instant and then settled down to a bright glow. He replaced the glass and began to dress.

The farmer suddenly winced sharply and abruptly walked back to the kitchen, hoping Harold hadn't noticed. So far no one knew about the trouble he'd been having breathing lately, culminating yesterday with the ragged pain that had bloomed in his chest while he was alone in the barn. He had sunk to a sitting position with his back against a stall and the barbed needles of pain had gradually withdrawn, leaving him weak and frightened.

He hadn't told Ida because he knew only too well what her reaction would be. She'd get scared and begin to badger him all over again about going to a doctor for a check-up. James W. Porter did not cotton to doctors, but for the first time he felt himself beginning

Finette Fox was moved in spite of herself by the gravity of her husband's voice. She touched his arm and said, "You really believe this flood is coming, don't you."

"I was never more sure of anything," he declared. "You remember back in '98 when I said the flood was coming and we did get a pretty bad one?"

She nodded reluctantly. Every time anyone ever mentioned his false alarms, he always brought up the flooding of 1898 which he had predicted accurately — when five feet of water had covered North Dayton and the sewers in their own neighborhood had backed up and there'd been three feet of water in the streets and yards.

"Well," he continued, "it's worse this time. Much worse. I stood on the bank and checked the rise of the water. It's about four feet from the top of the levee right now. Three hours ago it was at least eight feet below the top. And now it seems like it's rising even faster than before. Believe me, Fin, this is it. This is the big one I've known for years was coming."

She had to admit to herself, she was impressed. His warning this time was different, more sure of itself, more believable. She slid out of bed and started dressing. For the first time in his many years of flood prediction, she was beginning to be afraid he was right.

✳ 4 A.M.
TUESDAY

Police sergeant Homer Tupman and his partner, patrolman W. T. Jenkins, began their house-to-house evacuation of residents in their assigned area on the near West Side along the Wolf Creek levee at just after two-thirty. In an hour and a half they'd convinced some two hundred families that they'd better move out, and the streets were lively with people heading toward the slopes to the west.

It was about this time that the streets began filling with water. Within forty minutes the water was gushing from the occasional unclosed sewers as if they were fountains, and within an hour they were wading in at least twenty inches of water. Neither man had ever seen the water coming into the streets so rapidly before.

"Y'know, Sarge," Jenkins said, "damned if I don't think we're going to have a whing-ding of a flood this time."

Tupman didn't reply but his face was set in hard lines. He'd just been thinking the very same thing.

✳ 4:30 A.M.
TUESDAY

The presses of the Dayton *Journal* began rolling at high speed now with the flood extra, but it would be at least ninety minutes before delivery could even begin. Still, it might be of some help to those who had not yet heard the warnings. Delivery would be made in the most imperiled areas first, and the paper minced no words. The headline was a single bold black word: WARNING!

This was followed by a variety of stories with subheads that clarified the danger immediately:

FLOOD STAGE IN MIAMI RIVER RAPIDLY NEARED

NATIONAL GUARD ALERTED

[22]

RIVER GAUGE REGISTERS 16′6″ AT MIDNIGHT — 18′8″ AT 2:30 A.M.

AT 23 FEET WATER WILL FLOW OVER LEVEE

POLICE AND FIRE DEPARTMENTS HAVE BEEN MARSHALED

BREAK IN DAM IMMINENT IN LEVEE SOUTH OF STEELE DAM ON RIVERDALE SIDE

SAFETY DIRECTOR MAYS DODDS, FIRE CHIEF ED RAMBY, POLICE CHIEF JOHN ALLABECK PATROL ALL THREATENED CITY DISTRICTS IN DODDS' POWERFUL AUTO

ALL COMPANIES OF OHIO NATIONAL GUARD CALLED OUT TO HELP RESCUE FLOODED PEOPLE

DAYTON UNION RAILROAD COMPANY MOVES STRING OF HEAVY COAL CARS ONTO BRIDGE TO SAVE IT

TELEPHONE SERVICE RAPIDLY GOING OUT OF SERVICE AS CABLE SEWERS FLOOD

It was a commendable effort, but unfortunately it came just a little too late. Fewer than one-tenth of the newspapers being printed now would ever be delivered.

✳ 4:45 A.M.
TUESDAY

James W. Porter tapped the blanket-covered form of his son. The boy moaned and the farmer shook him lightly.

[23]

to waver. Maybe it wouldn't be a bad idea to go, just to satisfy her. There wasn't a thing wrong with him, he knew that. Hell, a man had to expect to get certain miseries as he got older. But . . . well, maybe he ought to go just to please Ida.

He was pulling on his thin denim jacket as Harold clumped into the kitchen, took down his own jacket from the hook by the back door and put it on. He hesitated for a moment and cocked an ear toward the rain peppering the roof.

"Sure gettin' our share of rain this spring, Pa," he said. "Keeps on this way an' the west field'll get flooded again."

"Uh-huh," Porter grunted. He was glad the house and barn were on the highest ground of the farm. Three years ago this month the Miami River, a quarter mile to the west, had gone over its banks and dumped eighteen inches of water into that field. Of course, the rain they'd been having the past couple of days didn't seem quite as hard as that one had been, but apparently it was pretty widespread. If they'd had very much to the north, there'd probably be some more flooding.

"Let's hope not, son," he said. "Not after all the work we did last summer getting them fences strung tight again." The cows were lowing even more loudly now and Porter ruffled Harold's hair and grinned. "Let's get to the milkin', boy."

He opened the door and stepped out onto the porch and then stopped so suddenly that Harold bumped into him. "God almighty!" he said.

"What's the matter, Pa?" Harold stepped around him

and stopped just as shortly as he, too, saw the water.

There were two wooden steps up to the porch from yard level and neither could be seen. A blanket of rapidly flowing muddy water hissed past less than two inches from porch level. It looked as if they were in a big houseboat surrounded by sea. The continued bellowing of the seven cows in the barn took on a new meaning now. Harold found his voice first.

"Gosh, Pa, it's water. It's a *flood!*" He was frightened, and his voice had become squeaky. "What're we gonna do, Pa?"

There was only one thing to do. Porter took his son by the shoulder and spoke rapidly but calmly. "Hop back into the house an' get your ma an' sisters up. Tell 'em to dress warm. Don't scare 'em, but tell 'em to hurry. We got to get out of here. That water ain't finished comin' up yet. Now hop to it. I'll hitch up the wagon."

He stepped gingerly into the water, which was three or four inches below his knees in depth, and surged off toward the barn. For an instant Harold watched him go, fighting off a mounting panic. Then he raced into the old house.

✳ 5 A.M.
TUESDAY

Samuel Blackburn was an extremely punctual man, which may have been the reason why, at thirty-five, he was still unmarried. His daily life was regulated, when he was at home, by the fine old Seth Thomas clock on the mantel of the comfortable frame house at 30 Fairgrounds Avenue where he lived with his mother.

Maude Blackburn was just as punctual as her son. Indeed, it was she who had taught him the traits which guided his life. When he was a child she had stood him before the same clock many times, and her words were deeply etched in his mind.

"Time," she always said gravely, "can be your friend or your enemy. If you treat it with respect and conserve rather than waste it, you will be a successful man. Time is God's gift to man and you are alloted only so much of it in your lifetime. There is never enough of it to merely fritter it away on meaningless activities."

Sam Blackburn had learned this lesson well, and time had become not only his guide but his constant companion, his director, the dictating factor of his life. It is perhaps significant that for his graduation from high school when he was eighteen, Blackburn had received as a gift from his mother a beautifully etched and engraved gold pocket watch. He never went anywhere without it and carried the motto engraved upon it in his head as well as on the watch:

Time is the enemy only of those who are enemies of Time.

For seventeen years now he had carried this watch faithfully and it guided his outside activities as surely as did the mantel clock when he was at home. And though the fine floral etching was worn smooth in several places, the watch was just as beautiful and ticked away the seconds and minutes and hours just as accurately as it had when it was new.

When the mantel clock chimed five this morning, Sam Blackburn awakened on the last note as if it had been an alarm set to rouse him. He wasted little time in performing his toilet and donning the blue shirt and gray trousers and vest he had laid out the night before. He prepared his usual breakfast of one fried egg, two strips of bacon, one slice of toast and a cup of coffee.

As usual, the clock was chiming the three-quarters hour when he left the house. A steady rain was still falling, and the air had a penetrating chill to it. He was glad he had worn his rubbers and heavy jacket. He raised his umbrella and walked the short distance to South Main Street where he turned north toward downtown.

Although short in stature — scarcely four inches over five feet — Sam Blackburn walked with a strong, distance-eating pace. Each working day for the past eight years he had walked to and from his job at the Barney and Smith Car Company almost two miles distant. He had never been late to work, nor had he ever arrived more than three minutes early, giving himself time to remove his coat, get into his coveralls and start his painting of the interiors of new railroad coaches.

Six blocks north, at the corner of Vine and Main, Blackburn paused to watch old Mr. Saettel open his little cafe and grocery. He liked Ollie Saettel very much and so, it seemed, did everyone else. The old man opened his doors about six each morning, and the fact that he rarely had any customers — other than Blackburn — until after seven made little difference. He had been opening at six and closing at eight in the evening for as long as he had been in business here, and though occasionally Sam Blackburn discreetly hinted that opening so early was just wasting his time, the old man merely chuckled and fell back on his often repeated adage that old dogs can't be taught new tricks.

"Good morning, Ollie," Blackburn said. "No customers yet?" This was the usual preamble to their conversation, and Saettel answered his usual way.

"Nope. Just Sam Blackburn. How you doing this morning, Sam?"

"Fine. Just fine. Nasty day, though, isn't it?"

Saettel bobbed his unkempt gray head. "Looks like the rain's finally going to ease up a little today, though. Been a mighty weird sky these past two days." He filled a cup of coffee and set it in front of Blackburn, who stirred in a half teaspoonful of sugar and nodded in return.

"I suppose," he said thoughtfully, "it's the tail end of that cyclone that hit Omaha on Easter. Understand it did a terrible amount of damage."

"They can be bad, awful bad," Saettel said. "Glad we don't get anything like that in the Miami Valley. Just lots of rain." He chuckled again.

Both men looked toward the front window as the big NCR factory whistle blew. After awhile it stopped, then started to blow again. In a few minutes a second, then a third whistle blew and, a little later, a church bell began tolling. The men looked at each other.

"Now what d'ye suppose that's for?" Ollie Saettel asked.

"Fire," Blackburn said. "Probably a big one downtown." He shook his head slowly. "Funny they'd make such a fuss though. They never did that before. Well, we'll find out about it soon enough, I guess."

Blackburn drained his cup and Saettel immediately refilled it. The painter took out his watch, opened it and noted that it was now several minutes after six. He also noted with some concern that the link of the gold chain nearest the watch was worn so thin that even a slight pull would probably break it. Thankful he had spotted it in time, he unhooked the fob end of the chain from his vest buttonhole and put the chain into the vest pocket with the watch.

"Almost worn through," he told Saettel, noting the old man watching him. "I'll have to try to fix it tonight."

"Fine-looking watch," Saettel said, as he'd said numerous times before. He was more familiar with Blackburn's watch than he was with his own, at which he seldom bothered to look.

A glow of pride suffused through the younger man and he smiled. "I like it," he said. "Never loses a minute and I've had it seventeen years now." The conversation was almost a verbatim repeat of other conversations through the years, but both men played the game and acted as if it were a newly discovered topic. Outside, the whistles continued blowing and now another church bell added to the din.

"Reckon that fire must be a pretty bad one," Saettel said. "Mary'll probably tell me all about it when she gets in." Mary Schunk was a waitress at Saettel's who arrived at seven each morning and left at four. As a result, Blackburn had never seen her, but he knew her well from Ollie

Saettel's frequent references to her and her husband, Ed, a barber in the downtown Arcade.

"I expect she'll know what happened," Blackburn agreed. "Ed'll probably call her or she'll call him. Then she'll tell you and tomorrow morning you can give me the whole story."

He finished drinking the second cup of coffee, put a nickel on the counter and took out his watch again. It was 6:10 A.M. and he was right on time. At the door he turned and tossed a wave to Saettel. "So long," he said. "Don't do anything I wouldn't do."

"What wouldn't you do, Sam?" said the old man, smiling.

That was the way they parted every working morning.

✳ 5:15 A.M.
TUESDAY

When James Porter brought the team and wagon to the house, the water was within a quarter of an inch of running across the porch and into the kitchen. He had to talk reassuringly to the horses and keep a tight grip on the bridles to keep them under control.

Out in the barn he had opened the door to let the cows out, except for the pair tethered to the rear of the wagon. These two were his best producers and he had decided to save them if at all possible. The others would have to fend for themselves.

The pair of Holsteins strained and tugged at the thongs holding them to the tailgate of the open wagon. The cold water was already swirling about their udders and their eyes rolled in fear and they bellowed and grunted constantly.

Ida was standing on the porch with a lantern and the girls — sixteen-year-old Flossie, twelve-year-old Goldie and ten-year-old Shirley — clustered near her. Shirley was crying. Harold came outside carrying an armload of blankets, which he dumped on an old chair on the porch.

"You all right, Jim?" Ida asked, putting a hand on his arm as he tied the reins securely to the porch post. "You're all wet. You'll catch cold."

"No help for it," he said shortly, then squeezed her hand to take the sting out of the reply. "Don't worry, we'll be all right. Ground's higher on Troy Pike. We'll be all right."

"We gathered a lot of things to take along, Papa," said Flossie. She was a tall, pretty girl with long straw-colored hair. Her cheeks were flushed with excitement and she didn't seem at all frightened. "We stacked 'em up in the kitchen." She turned to reenter the house but Porter stopped her.

"No!" He shook his head vigorously. "Weight of us six in the wagon's gonna be enough for Tom an' Belle as it is. They're gonna have a hard time pullin' us through the muck an' water. We got no time to waste. Everybody in the wagon. Come on, Shirl, you first."

He picked up his youngest daughter under his arms and swung her into the wagon bed. "Now you crouch down here an' hold on," he ordered. "We'll get some blankets to cover you an' keep you a mite warm."

In a few minutes all four children and their mother were huddled together in the wagon bed. Porter tossed two blankets over them. "These'll get wet, but at least they help keep off the rain a little."

The children seemed to find a comfort in the closeness and their fears subsided somewhat. The cows stood dumbly behind, occasionally jerking at their tethers but no longer crying out and apparently resigned to getting very wet.

Porter entered the house a last time and blew out the lamp. In the darkness he clutched his chest as a sharp pain stabbed him. It faded away quickly and he went out, closing the door after him. The water was on the porch now and just beginning to trickle over the door sill and into the kitchen.

"All set back there?" he called, taking his seat.

"All set!"

"Here we go now," he said. "We'll be safe in Dayton." He whacked the reins against the horses' rumps. "G'yupp!" Tom and Belle strained against the drag of water and mud and the wagon lurched and began rolling.

They were on their way to safety.

✳ 5:30 A.M.
TUESDAY

John H. Patterson had not slept well, and this was most unusual for him, since even the most pressing of matters rarely interfered with his sleep. He used no alarm clock, yet always awoke at 5:45 A.M. and arrived at his office in the National Cash Register Company at six-thirty. Punctuality, he had often said, is a great virtue.

On this Tuesday morning, however, he had awakened

[33]

at 4:40 A.M. and lain in bed a short time listening to the persistent dripping from the eaves. During the innumerable times he had roused during the night the same sound had always been there. He had known at this final awakening that further sleep would not come, and he arose.

Now, after a light breakfast and two cups of coffee, he rang for his car. The great old clock in the hallway of his estate, Far Hills, solemnly bonged the half hour.

Fifteen minutes later he stepped out of the car in front of NCR and told his driver to wait. He went directly to his office, calling Barringer in behind him as he passed through the outer office. If the secretary was surprised to see the president three-quarters of an hour earlier than usual, he did not show it.

Barringer stood quietly by, unquestioning but ready for any instructions that might come. Patterson walked directly to his window and looked out. His eyes widened. The Great Miami River looked nearly half again as large as it had the previous afternoon.

He next went to the roof and carefully studied not only the river's condition where it left Dayton just opposite NCR a half mile to the west, but also where Wolf Creek entered it near West Third Street, where the Mad River entered from the east and the Stillwater River from the north. All of them — including the Great Miami entering Dayton from the northeast — were running bank full.

Patterson had seen Dayton suffer minor flooding many times over the past threescore years, and usually it had been caused by one or two of the rivers overflowing while the other two or three remained only slightly higher than normal. Once only — in 1866 — three of the rivers had been at flood stage. But this was the first time all four rivers were full to the point of overflowing as far as the eye could see upstream.

Without a word he turned and reentered the building, Barringer only slightly behind him. On the way down he instructed his secretary, "Call the Powerhouse. From now until I cancel it, I want the whistle blown at one-minute intervals for thirty seconds."

Barringer dipped his head and made the call from his office as Patterson waited. Then they went downstairs together, got into the car and drove along the downtown levees. Twice they passed small squads of National Guardsmen, but though Patterson took note of them, he made no comment. Nor did he remark about the abnormal number of police and firemen on the streets.

Everywhere they went there were crowds of people standing on the levees watching the fascinating spectacle of over one hundred thousand cubic feet of water passing every second. On the levee along Monument Avenue there were literally hundreds of people, with the most congested area between Main Street and Monument Avenue. Patterson tapped his driver on the shoulder.

"Stop," he said and added, turning to Barringer, "Wait here."

He got out and climbed the levee just behind the Central Fire Station. At the top, fifteen feet above street level, he was shaken in spite of himself at the sight of the river running past with an evil swishing less than five inches from the top.

Spectators huddling under umbrellas talked and laughed and gazed in wonder at the force of the water, but none seemed particularly concerned. Scattered comments reached Patterson's ears over the whistles and the church bells.

"Just look at 'er. Ain't that something!"

"By golly, I never seen it this high before."

"Lowlands'll be flooded sure, this keeps up."

"'Spose it might run over?"

"Hell, no! Ain't raining half as hard now as it was an hour ago."

"Whoo-eee! Look at that river! Hey, May Jean, Jerry, y'all come up here an' take a looksee."

Disgusted, Patterson turned abruptly and half slid back down the slope. His nostrils flared and his brows pinched down in an angry glare. He slammed the door hard.

"Back to the office," he told the driver, leaning back in the seat. He shook his head. "The fools!" he said softly, bitterly. "The incredible fools!"

At the door to his office he turned to Barringer. "I'm calling a full-scale executive meeting at exactly six forty-five. In the large conference room. I want all of them. No excuses."

Barringer glanced at the clock. It was six thirty-five.

✽ 6:00 A.M.
TUESDAY

Troy Pike had water on it, but at least it wasn't very deep. Behind him in the wagon bed, James Porter could hear his wife and children singing. He recognized the tune as a hymn but didn't know the words.

The pain in his chest had come again, and this time it

stayed. A dull throbbing ache filled his left side, and his leg seemed to have gone to sleep. He hunched down miserably, as much to make himself a smaller target for the persistent rain as to prevent the chest pain from worsening.

He wished now that he had left the cows behind. They had badly slowed the wagon's progress. Even in those two high areas where the road had been free of water, their progress had been slow and Tom and Belle had been forced to work harder than they should have. He wished he could stop and rest them, but didn't dare.

He breathed a little easier when the roughly paved road turned to brick, indicating they were entering North Dayton. Belle's hooves momentarily slid from beneath her and she thrashed frantically to regain her footing. Ahead the water looked even deeper and Porter wondered if they'd make it to Uncle Erman's house near Valley Pike. He remembered how his uncle had told stories about the flood of 1866 and how the water had surged about their house to a depth of six feet, but the house was big and well built and safe. He had often told them to come to his house for safety at the first sign of high water.

Far in the distance a whistle blew, then another, still a third. A church bell clanged noisily not far away. In the gray light of dawn smudging the sky, Porter noted the streets were almost empty. Far down Troy Pike toward Valley Street he saw two horsemen surge across the street and disappear. As his own wagon crossed the intersection of Leo Street, he saw another horse with two riders in the east, belly-deep.

Harold poked his head from under the covers. "Listen

to the whistles an' bells, Pa!" he said. "They must be warnin' people that — *PA!*"

Porter spun around at the sudden terror in his son's voice. A paralyzing chill struck him as he saw what had frightened Harold — a huge foaming wave heading toward them from several hundred yards behind. It was about four feet high. A similar and only slightly smaller wave was coming from the west on Leo.

"Hee-yah!" He slashed the reins across the horses' rumps and the animals plunged forward, sliding and stumbling. They didn't have a chance. Before they'd gone thirty feet the wave from behind hit them, sweeping both cows from their feet and dragging them around toward the front. The wagon turned broadside to the current and the two upstream wheels lifted high.

For an agonizing moment it balanced there as Porter fought to control it, dimly hearing the screams of the girls behind him. Then the wave from Leo Street hit them and the wagon turned turtle. The tongue snapped and the traces pulled loose, freeing the horses.

Porter was catapulted far into the rampaging current, and even as he hit the icy water he felt the incredibly sharp pain burst in his chest. He lost consciousness before he could fight his way to the surface.

Under the overturned wagon, the children seized one another in their panic, hanging on desperately even as their breaths exploded from them with the shock of the frigid water. Inextricably tangled with one another and with the blankets wrapped about them besides, they had no chance and their struggles quickly ceased.

Ida Porter had started to get to her feet when Harold shouted his warning, and when the wagon pitched over she was thrown out and landed between the two cows and as one of them tossed its head frantically, its short horn caught her shoulder and tore it open to the bone. A hoof slammed into the small of her back, thrusting her under the water, but she fought her way back and broke surface thirty feet from the wagon, which bobbed along with its wheels in the air.

A board hissed through the water and slapped her face a stunning blow, gouging her cheek, yet she managed to keep her head up, floating helplessly with the powerful current. She struck a tree, tried to hold on but was bounced back into the current. Her left side bumped agonizingly into a metal hitching post beneath the surface and she felt something tear inside her, but there was no pain and vaguely she wondered why.

The wagon had lodged against a picket fence far behind her but she did not know it. For a short while her world was a queer one, dissociated from physical sensation, her mind withdrawn from her body, somehow trying to realize that this chip of life being carried along was her own.

The current whirled her to a storefront, thrust her partially through the jagged remains of the big plate glass window and then pulled her out again. The right side of her head in front of her ear, from scalpline to neck, was laid open and turned the dirty water to russet nearby.

A telephone pole jutted from the water ahead, and as she swept into it her right arm managed to crook around a foot spike. She dangled there a little while as the water tugged to pull her free and, when unable to do so by itself, performed the job with an implement.

A slope-roofed outhouse came bobbing swiftly along and smashed to flinders against the pole, breaking her arm as well as her hold. She was now afloat again, already nearly a half mile from where the wagon overturned, still alive in some miraculous fashion, still aware in some deep recess of her mind that somehow she must get herself out of the water. But then, as she was swept across the intersection of Light Street, an eddy caught her and whirled her bodily into a brick wall of a building and she sank.

Her body continued to tumble under the water until her legs became tangled in a broken electric wire and she thudded heavily into the wall of a big white house at 206 Troy Pike. The current pinned her snugly under the porch eave. An elderly man and woman in the upper front bedroom heard the noise of her striking and looked at one another.

"What was *that*, Erm?" the woman asked.

"Just some floatin' debris hittin' the house, I reckon," he answered. He walked to the window and looked out again at the chilling sight of the water rushing past. "Six — seven feet deep out there already." He shook his head. "Reckon they's no chance of Jim an' his family gettin' here now."

✳ 6:10 A.M.
TUESDAY

The sounding of the flood alarms — though she didn't know that's what they were — jerked Mary Althoff awake and for a long moment in the gray light of her bedroom she listened to them, wondering if she were still dreaming. She decided she wasn't and went to the window to look out.

"Gloomy and miserable, just like yesterday," she grumbled. Below her the gutters of East Second Street were running full. Here and there an occasional pedestrian moved along quickly beneath the dubious protection of an umbrella or dodged from doorway to doorway in a vain attempt to keep from getting drenched.

"The lowlands," she murmured, considering the bells and whistles. "They're flooding again and the people are being warned." She shook her head and grimaced. While she sympathized with them in their plight, she couldn't understand why people insisted on living in those low areas, knowing as they did that every time the heavy rains came their basements and sometimes even their living rooms suffered inundation.

Head of the circulation department at the Dayton Public Library on the eastern edge of the downtown sector, Mary Althoff wasn't due at work until 8:30 A.M. Normally she arose at seven o'clock, ate a leisurely breakfast while reading the morning *Journal,* did up her dishes and then walked the two blocks to work. Now she frowned as she glanced at the big alarm clock perched on her dresser.

She contemplated going back to bed but then she shrugged. The clamor outside would probably keep her awake anyway. She decided to stay up and perhaps take care of some of the mending that needed to be done. After another glance out of the window she walked to the hall closet and fumbled about in the darkness for her heavy rubber overshoes.

She sighed as she set them on the floor by the front door so she wouldn't forget to put them on. She hated wearing them because they made her legs tired after walking only a short distance, but from the looks of the water running in the gutters this morning, she just might need them before she reached the library.

✳ 6:29 A.M.
TUESDAY

Samuel P. Blackburn checked into work at precisely 6:29 A.M., disturbed by the fact that he was a minute or so later than usual, due to the fact that he'd had to make detours in several places to avoid great spouts of water gushing up from storm sewers. The Miami Canal, beside which he had to walk for a half mile, had been full almost to the point of overflowing and raced by with a speed he'd never seen it exhibit during the eight years he'd walked this route, not even after the heaviest of rainstorms.

Numerous times he had been forced to step into ankle-deep water, so his rubbers hadn't done him much good. He knew his mother would be concerned when she found out — as he knew she would — that he'd been at work all day with wet feet.

Work did not start until six-thirty at the Barney and Smith Car Company during normal times, but this morning it didn't start at all. Most of the men were concerned about the height of the Mad River a block to the north of them. It was apparent that there was some pretty serious flooding, and Blackburn's foreman, Mike McDill, suggested they go to the levee to see if they could help anyone.

All the men were deeply shocked when they got there and saw for themselves the angry yellowish-brown water ripping by less than a foot from where they were standing — and right at this point the levee was nearly thirty feet above street level. But the biggest shock was the condition of North Dayton on the other side of the river, where the water was already swirling around the houses in depths of six to seven feet. Here and there they could see people on rooftops, and almost directly across the river a horse and mule stood together in misery on the roof of a stable which they'd apparently reached by climbing a ramp.

"My gosh," McDill muttered, "they're really flooded over there this time."

Since it was the lowest section of the city, the men had often seen North Dayton with water in its streets, but they'd never seen it look as it looked now.

Blackburn looked downstream along the levee on which they were standing toward Taylor Street. The water couldn't get very much higher without sliding over the top, and once that happened the earth would erode quickly. If the levee were to break, the whole of downtown might be flooded.

To the east the water wasn't quite as close to the levee top, but it was still threatening. And upstream, on the far side of the river, Blackburn saw a chilling sight. From the roof of a small shed which was all but covered, an elderly man was helping a young woman with a baby in her arms to scale a ladder reaching to the top of a low adjoining dwelling with a flat roof. The side of the roof where they stood was already under water and the current whipped about them fiercely. Blackburn could see they were fighting to keep from being swept off their feet. He was sure that as soon as the woman and child made it to the roof the ladder would be swept away and the old man with it. Miraculously, however, as the young woman braced it from above, the old man managed to make it to the top. He tried to pull the ladder up after him but it was wrenched from his grasp and whirled away.

The three were safe now, but only temporarily. If the water kept rising or the foundation was eaten away and the little house collapsed, there'd be little chance for them.

Blackburn began to run upstream along the levee. On an unseasonably warm day a week ago he'd walked up the levee during his lunch hour and about a block from this spot he'd seen a rowboat tied to a tree and lying upside down.

He was panting when he reached the boat and turned it over. It wasn't new but it looked seaworthy. A tough cord knotted it to the tree and he looked around for something to cut it with. He had no knife and there was nothing on the ground nearby with a sharp edge. The knots were pulled so tight it would take much time to unloosen them. He shot a look back across the river.

The man and woman both waved and apparently they were calling to him, but he couldn't hear them. As he watched, the house suddenly made a half turn, throwing the couple in a heap on top. Then it remained steady again.

Desperately Blackburn searched the area and found two large rocks. He put one on the ground and placed the cord over it and with the other he beat at the fiber furiously until it spread, frayed and then broke apart. He righted the boat and slid it to the water's edge, where he launched it and then hopped in. Too late the realization came that there were no oars.

He tried to paddle with his hands, but against this current it was useless. He was now about twenty feet from the levee and moving sideways, gaining momentum all the time.

As he passed Webster Street he had to duck his head to miss the concrete bridge spanning the stream, and he heard Mike McDill and his co-workers shouting at him, but it was all he could do to hang on. The floating debris that kept hitting the boat did not make it any easier.

Now he shot into the area where the Mad River joins the Great Miami and the rivers were more than rivers — they were lakes with a powerful current. Blackburn's feet were cold, and looking down he was horrified to see there were already five inches of water in the boat.

Ahead of him downstream he could see the Main Street

bridge, and just this side of the bridge on the downtown side of the river the levee was milling with a great crowd of people. He waved at them frantically, but there was nothing anyone could do and so they just stood there, fascinated at the sight of him rushing downstream.

All at once the entire crowd turned as one and fled screaming down the slope. In a few seconds the levee had become devoid of human life. As he approached the spot, the reason for the hurried departure became obvious to Blackburn. The water of the river was pouring over the top of the levee and down into the city.

"Oh, those people, those people!" he cried. He was certain none of them would survive.

The water in his boat was now less than two inches from the gunwales and he knew he'd have to get out. The Main Street bridge was his only chance. Having become filled with water, the boat moved sluggishly. He was floating only twenty feet or so from the overflowing levee, but it was obvious that his momentum would carry him past the opening. The bridge ahead spanned the water in a great gentle arch. The center was still six feet out of the water but near the ends, like the one he was now approaching, it was only a foot out of the water.

As the boat neared the structure Blackburn crouched on the center seat facing it, timing himself. When he leaped, his body slammed against the iron railing driving the breath from him in a great whoosh. His boat disappeared beneath the bridge and he clung with all his strength to the metal. The rail itself hummed and thumped with the transmitted sound of the rushing waters and objects striking the bridge from below.

When his breath began coming more easily he pulled himself up and over the railing, tumbling in a heap on the boarded sidewalk. The stability of the bridge, its firmness beneath him, was a wonderful thing, and it revived him more than anything else. He smiled briefly. What a story he'd have to tell Mother tonight!

Then he remembered the old man, woman and baby on the roof and he sat upright. Upstream he could see a great deal of floating debris, but nothing indicating life. To the south, toward downtown, the water was rushing madly down Main Street and appeared to be about a foot deep already at Third and Main, the city's principal intersection and dividing point for east and west, north and south. In the distance he could see people wading through it, horses pulling wagons crowded with people. Even as he watched most of these people were disappearing into buildings toward safety.

To the north the water was even deeper, rushing toward him down Main Street to the foot of the bridge and then turning west to race down Lehman Street toward McKinley Park, making his bridge a veritable island in the raging waters. Many of the windows in the Bellevue Apartments at the northeast edge of the bridge were filled with spectators watching this great drama unfold.

Faintly he heard a scream and looked upstream. The first thing he saw was a horse only a dozen yards away, its eyes bulging in terror as it hurtled toward the bridge and struggling frantically to keep its head above water. The scream came again, a little louder now, and he saw the little house floating toward him. At first he was not sure it was the same one he'd seen from the levee because

[47]

only the woman and child were there, she clinging tightly to the roof with one hand and just as desperately to the babe with the other.

They were just a little to the north of mid-stream, and he ran along the bridge, reaching the spot where they would pass with plenty of time to spare. Carefully he climbed over the railing and lowered himself to the outside abutment. The house was almost certain to strike the pillar, and the rescue would have to be timed perfectly.

Straddling the top of the abutment, he gripped it tightly with his heels as if he were riding a horse. The woman saw him and rose from her sitting position to a crouch. The house rode low in the water, the roof just slightly sloped and no more than a foot abve the surface. He could hear the baby squalling.

"Come as close as you can toward this edge of the roof," Blackburn hollered. "Hang on until just before you reach me. When I yell 'Now!,' stand up straight and raise your free arm. Can you do it?"

"Yes," she called back and he was amazed at her calmness. She scrambled to the leading edge of the roof and crouched there. They were only thirty feet apart and the distance closed quickly.

"Now!"

Instantly she stood erect, swayed a little and regained her balance. Holding the lower rail of the bridge with his left hand, Blackburn bent, scooped and felt his arm encircle her waist from the front. Her upraised arm came down across his nose and eyes, gripping tightly. Although he couldn't see it, he heard the hideous grinding crash as the house struck the abutment and broke into many pieces.

His left arm felt as if it would pull from its socket as he slowly pulled himself upright. "Grab the rail!" he ordered, still unable to see. "Hang tight until I can lift you higher."

He felt her arm leave his head and some of her weight ease off as she clasped the rail. He relinquished his own hold on it and put his left arm around her, lifted her up until her knees found a purchase on the pillar top. Then they stood up together, he with one arm still about her waist, holding her. The baby continued to wail. From the direction of the Bellevue Apartments he heard cheering.

He helped her over the rail to safety and then followed her. Downstream he could see large chunks of the house turning over and swirling in the current as they were whirled off. He turned to the girl.

"Where is the old . . . where's . . ."

"My father?" she asked quietly. "He . . . he slid into the water when the house broke loose. I don't think . . . he didn't come up."

Deeply sorry for her, Blackburn led the girl to the north end of the bridge. The water between there and the entrance to the Bellevue was under only a couple of feet of water and there was little current here. He carried them to the door, opened it and gently placed her on the stairs. When he turned to go out again she stopped him.

"Wait. I . . . I want to thank you. We saw you get the boat and try to help us. My father said you were a very brave man. You are. Thank you."

Blackburn grinned. For the first time in his thirty-five

years he felt that he'd really done something worthwhile. He felt big and strong and important. It was a good feeling and he waved as he waded out the door.

Somewhat lightheaded and feeling foolishly invincible, he returned to the middle of the bridge and saw that only an occasional person or horse was visible on Main Street downtown. The water was already well over the wagon hubs and some of the lighter ones had turned over and were bumping along to the south.

He looked up the river and saw no other marooned people, but there was a beautiful collie coming his way in the bed of a floating wagon. The dog was soaking wet and cringed pitifully against the side of the wagon, its feet widespread to maintain balance. It was wearing a collar, and Blackburn felt sure he could snatch the collar and swing the dog up onto the bridge.

The current would bring the wagon to almost the exact center of the bridge and he'd have to lean far to grab the dog. Once more he located the correct position and climbed the rail. There was no pillar here and he had to crouch on the narrow rim. He squatted with one hand on the lower rung of the railing and the other poised to grab.

As the wagon swept below him he dipped and his fingers slid under the dog's collar and clamped shut. As the weight of the animal slid off the wagon and pulled him down even more, a flash of gold caught his eye and he saw his watch pop from his vest pocket and begin falling slowly because it was dragging the chain out of his pocket behind it.

His beautiful watch! His graduation gift. The watch he'd lived by, eaten by, worked by for seventeen years!

Instinctively, without conscious volition, his left hand released the rail and snatched for the watch. He fell.

The bitterly cold water swept him under and, though he lost his hold on the dog, he managed to catch the watch, and he gripped the timepiece firmly in his fist. He had not taken a deep breath and he fought to reach the surface. He felt something bump his back. It was the dog and it braced its legs against his shoulders and shoved him down as it tried to reach the surface.

A smothering blackness closed over Samuel Blackburn and he thought of the words on the watch: *Time is the enemy only of those who are enemies of Time.*

His struggles ceased and he relaxed, and the fine gold watch slipped from his fingers and was gone.

Time had run out for Samuel Blackburn.

✳ 6:30 A.M.
TUESDAY

J. Harvey Kirkbride's curiosity finally got the best of him and he walked out on the front porch of his house at 318 West Fourth Street and waved down the next carriage that clattered toward him. The man holding the reins pulled up reluctantly.

"What's the matter?" Kirkbride asked. "What's going on?"

"Warning's gone out for people to get out of the downtown area," said the man, struggling to keep the nervous horse from prancing about. "That's what all the bells and whistles are about. Water's almost to the tops of the levees and they're saying downtown's going to get hit bad.

Me, I'm heading for the hills in East Dayton. Want to ride along?"

Kirkbride grinned. This wasn't the first time there had been a high water scare and timid folks started heading for high ground. He shook his head. "No thanks. I'll be all right, but thanks for the offer."

The man shrugged and flicked the reins and the horse cantered forward, turned south on Wayne Avenue and disappeared. Kirkbride scratched his chin. Well, if there was going to be some water in the streets he'd better get down to the office to make sure nothing would be damaged if the floors got wet. There were a number of cases of paper materials, both blank and already printed, near the back door of the Johnson and Watson Company at 131 East Third Street where Kirkbride was a book printer. He ought to get them to the second floor just in case.

Even when, between his house and the Miami Canal, he had to wade through a section of water halfway to his knees that was being forced up through a storm sewer, he wasn't worried. By the time he passed the Schwind Power Building at the triangular corner of Fourth, St. Clair and Kenton Streets, he was well away from the water again.

The rush of people heading away from the downtown area had disappeared now and many people strolled along the sidewalks on their way to work just as they did any other day. Harvey Kirkbride decided that, just like all the other times in the past which he remembered, it was a false alarm.

He hadn't taken time to eat at home so now he entered a little restaurant on East Third almost directly across

tives not yet here that they are to report immediately upon arriving."

"Good. Come along."

The pair entered the conference room and the voices stilled. Barringer took a seat in the front row while John Patterson stepped up on a low dais and stopped beside an easel holding a large blank tablet — standard equipment in every conference room and executive office at NCR. He picked up a heavy black crayon and swiftly sketched a neat pyramid of boxes, filling them with the names or initials of various executives. In the top box he printed J.H.P. While he was doing this, three more executives stepped into the room and quietly sat down. Patterson turned and looked at the stenographer — a young man — at a table to one side and nodded. "Take down," he directed.

"Gentlemen," he said, "a great disaster is going to fall on Dayton today and we must get ready for it. This sketch," he rapped the chart with his knuckles, "represents the organization known as the National Cash Register Company. As of this moment I declare NCR temporarily out of commission and proclaim this," he hit the chart again, "the Dayton Citizens' Relief Association."

There was an immediate low murmuring among the executives and astonished, even unbelieving, glances passed between them. However, their respectful silence quickly returned. They had long since learned two things; first, that John Patterson always had a good reason for what he did and, secondly, that people who interrupted him inconsequentially did not long remain NCR executives.

from his own office. He tapped the rain drops from his derby, shook his Cravenette and hung both on a hook near his seat.

"Coffee?" asked the man behind the counter.

"Uh-huh. Breakfast, too. Think I'll have some bacon strips and a couple of eggs fried sunny side up. Maybe that'll make the sun take a hint and peek through these clouds."

The cook grunted morosely. "Sure gettin' our share of it these past three days, ain't we? Gettin' so's I forget what sunshine looks like. Okay, bacon an' eggs comin' up."

"Mind if I look at your paper?" Kirkbride asked.

"Help yourself. Ain't much in it though, 'cept some stories about them tornadoes they had out in Nebraska. Sure glad we're in a valley here where we don't get bothered too much by winds like that. I went through a twister once, over in Missouri. Bad. Real bad. Feel a lot safer here. Wife's sister lived here so the old lady ragged me until I finally give in an' we moved here. Now she's always complainin' about her sinuses. Guy just can't win, can he?"

Kirkbride mumbled something but didn't look up from the paper, and the cook gave him a disgusted look and turned to his skillets.

✳ 6:35 A.M.
TUESDAY

The wagon paused at the top of the hill at North Main Street and Helena Avenue and the horse snorted impatiently. Both the man and the woman in the wagon — she holding an umbrella over them — looked tired. In the wagon was a jumble of goods over which a rumpled tarpaulin had been spread.

The woman looked down the Helena Street hill eastward toward the Great Miami River and saw that the low ground of Island Park on the opposite side of the bridge was already under water and that the expanse of flooding from that point stretched as far as they could see into North Dayton.

"You were right, Andy," she said. "All along you were right."

He grunted an affirmative. "I only wish," he said, "we'd been able to convince more people of it, Fin."

"Well, a surprising number of them believed you," she said soothingly.

He sniffed. "Not until the whistles began blowing. They believed them, not me. But now it may be too late for them to get out. They haven't got the time they think."

"What did the police say when you called them?" she asked. She had been upstairs, packing the last of the things she wanted to take, when he had called the police department around 4 A.M. to alert them of the danger.

"Well, they said a flood was possible," he said, but he seemed evasive. "They really didn't seem too concerned about it though. I did get them to admit," he added a bit proudly, "that I was the first to call in a warning. I'll bet now they wish they'd been more serious about it all. Well, they can't say we didn't warn them." He popped the reins and the horse began pulling them north on Main Street.

"No," Finette Fox admitted, "that's one thing they'll never be able to say."

✳ 6:45 A.M.
TUESDAY

The murmur filling the air of the conference room was decidedly strained. Something serious was in the wind, but none of them seemed to know even remotely what it might be. The intermittent wailing of the factory whistle was unnerving and irritating. Eyes snatched stealthy glimpses of the wall clock, their owners anxious for the meeting to begin.

Here were gathered the top men of the largest industry of its kind in the world. Here were gathered those who made it tick — the lawyers and scientists, accountants, engineers, inventors and mathematicians who, under the leadership of John H. Patterson, had built this firm into the largest privately owned company in a thriving multi-industrial metropolis. These were the first-line executives of the National Cash Register Company.

Not all of them were here, Barringer hastened to explain to the president one minute before the meeting was due to begin. Some had unaccountably failed to arrive at work that morning. Patterson nodded, not surprised.

"Perhaps," he said softly, getting to his feet, "more come in while our meeting is in progress. You've to have the whistle-blowing stopped until the meeting concluded?"

"Yes sir. And I've left word at the offices of the

"We here at NCR must prepare to house and feed the people of Dayton who will be driven from their homes when the city suffers a severe flood this morning." He paused and an executive stood and was recognized.

"Sir," he said, "this is a very startling thing. We are all aware Dayton has had considerable flooding in past years and never before has it required even limited aid from this firm, much less the literal conversion of the entire company into a relief organization for the city's population. What is there about today's possible flooding that makes it any different? How can you be so sure about it that you can willingly suspend our entire manufacturing operation and convert to a relief association," he paused and then blurted — ". . . before anyone apparently needs relief?"

"Well, now," Patterson said curtly, using the phrase that always presaged controlled anger on his part, "for one thing, I have studied the lay of this land in the Miami River Valley for years and I have always known that this was coming. I don't know how the city has escaped a wholly devastating flood this long, but I do know it will escape it no longer.

"To answer your questions specifically, however, our river banks — levees, if you will — are low. I have never had any faith in them as flood preventers. Land drainage, particularly above the city, is poor and the runoff high. The easiest way for this water to escape is through the city. Yet, our river channel is nearly twice as wide where it enters Dayton as where it leaves. A severe bend in the main river occurs at the edge of the downtown district and four rivers converge within one mile of this same downtown district. Through the years an abundance of debris has built up in the river bed in Dayton, helping that much more to retard the natural flow of the water. Had they been planned by a committee of expert hydraulic engineers, the existing conditions could hardly have been made better or more conducive for the occurrence of a great flood.

"The tops of the levees are approximately fifteen feet higher than the streets of downtown Dayton and, gentlemen," he said flatly, "I have just returned from an inspection of them. At this moment the rivers are ready to run over the tops of these levees. The resultant erosion will cause serious breaks and Dayton will be inundated today with the worst flood ever suffered by any major metropolitan area in the United States.

"Many of you," he added, glancing at the clock, "have wondered in the past why I chose to build this company here on a hill overlooking the city from the southern outskirts, when most other major industries are closer to the downtown sector and, as a result, better situated to railroads, principal highway arteries and the Miami Canal. It was no accident, gentlemen, I assure you. I did it because I have always expected what is happening right now."

He stopped talking and looked around the room. The executive had seated himself, and no one else spoke. He continued, "I did not call you here, however, to ask your opinions on whether or not NCR should become a relief organization for the duration of this disaster. I called you here to tell you your roles in it — and each and every one of you will play a major part, believe me. Commissary!"

A thin, bespectacled executive near the rear said "Yes, sir," and stood up.

"There will be a need for bread. Have a thousand loaves — no, two thousand — baked immediately. Have your cooks ready five hundred gallons of soup, more if possible. Prepare to serve all food supplies we have on hand and more. You're excused. Hydraulics."

Another executive, two seats from the first one, stood as the latter left.

"There will be a grave need for drinking water. City water will be no good within an hour or so. We will tap our own wells." He pointed to the pumping station in the field west of the factory. "If that is shut off, we will have no water supply. I want those engines kept running at all costs. Post a permanent crew there beginning now. Excused. Purchasing."

He was speaking rapidly now, clipping off his words sharply and causing the young stenographer to scribble frantically in order to keep pace. The portly executive sitting beside Barringer got up.

"Dispatch every person you can to the surrounding countryside and various areas in the city. Buy all the staple items of food you can find. Send trucks and wagons to the communities south and east of us — Centerville, Xenia, Lebanon, Franklin, Miamisburg, Middletown, Mason, Cincinnati — to buy the same items there. Also buy every cot, every bedstead available anywhere. Buy out all lots of blankets, pillows, work shirts and

trousers, cotton dresses, shoes of all sizes, boots, coveralls, gloves, hats. Excused. Communications."

His gaze centered on the young executive who snapped
to attention. "Immediately, using all available telephones
— and runners if the phones are inoperative — call every
principal city official, mayor, police, fire, water, electric.
Call every civic leader of note. Call every military office.
Inform them of what we are doing here. Ask their cooperation and help in all matters in my name. Excused.
Medical."

A tall gray individual stood, one of the three who had
arrived late. "Send out every man you have, plus a hundred good men selected from factory shop departments.
Have them pick up all available drugs — aspirin, iodine,
bandages, gauze, dressings, tapes, what have you — at
every drug store, pharmaceutical supply and hospital.
Tell the hosiptals what we are doing here and request
that word be sent to every doctor, nurse, medical attend-
ant or technician to report to NCR if at all possible.
Contact Coroner John McKemy and inform him as well.
Set up two emergency rooms, an isolaton ward, a morgue,
a nursery, a maternity ward. Excused. Sanitation."

No one stood up and there was an uncomfortable
shifting of feet and clearing of throats. Barringer shook
his head and Patterson jabbed a finger toward a departmental supervisor. "You're sanitation for the time being.
Secure, wherever available, all the disinfectant you can
find. Establish a constant watch over the NCR santitation
system to prevent blockage or back-up of pipes. Excused.
Security and Fire."

A huge grizzled man with a kindly face rose from his seat. "Yes, sir, Mr. Patterson."

"Handpick fifty men from among the foremen and job foremen not already engaged in emergency work. Brief them fully as an auxiliary but functioning police force. They will act as guards in and about the plant, prevent possible theft, rioting and looting here and elsewhere. No dispersal of firearms, however. Also form a fire extinguisher brigade and regular fire patrol. Excused."

For the first time he paused to look over the remaining faces, then pointed to a thin individual near the front. "Transportation. Locate every employee owning or capable of securing a motorcycle. Have them assemble at the garage and stand by as runners. No inexperienced men for this, it may be extremely difficult driving, even for the best. Secure every truck, every car, every wagon possible for transportation of goods and refugees. Supply each with a driver from among shop workers. Excused. Wood Working.

"There will be a grave need for boats to rescue marooned people. Draw up plans and templates for an easily constructed flat-bottomed stable rowboat that will safely seat six plus the rower. Start turning out boats and oars within an hour. We'll need at least two hundred of them. Excused. Safety."

Once again no one stood up and Patterson pointed to another departmental supervisor. "You're it. Organize a force of volunteers for rescue work. At least three hundred, better five hundred. Start them immediately toward the slopes leading up into the higher levels from downtown. They are not to walk closer into town than that.

The water will reach them soon enough. They are to remain at the high-water mark, effecting rescues among the citizens wherever possible. When the boats are built, assign men to them to penetrate flooded areas, concentrating mainly on moving people from precarious positions to safer positions. They are not to begin carrying marooned people to high ground until all those in highly precarious positions are moved to safety. Excused. Electrical.

"Dayton's electrical service will go out quickly. Transfer NCR's service to the emergency generators immediately. Excused."

The room had cleared out considerably now but Patterson didn't pause.

"Services. This building will be headquarters for everything. Basement for clothing salvage, disinfecting and dispersal. First floor for food service. Second floor, relief operations and military headquarters. Press also, since they'll be here quickly in large numbers. Third floor, general hospital. Fourth floor, maternity and nursery. Fifth, sixth, seventh floors, sleeping areas for men — put cots, beds and pallets in every available space. Eighth floor, barbers, cleaners, laundry, other services. Tenth and eleventh floors, women's quarters."

At last he stopped and brushed at his moustache with a knuckle. A dozen men were still in the room. "Gentlemen," he said, "the rest of you and the men beneath you will be called upon for various tasks. Questions, ideas, plans, all will be taken care of through Mr. Barringer. I will be spending the day on Main Street at the north foot of Fairgrounds Hill, where the water will reach by noon. You are all excused."

As the men left the room he stepped to the table, where the stenographer finished the last of his shorthand scrawls and flexed his hand slowly. Patterson squeezed his shoulder and smiled at him. "Good job, son," he said.

The wall clock clicked to exactly 7 A.M. In 15 minutes John H. Patterson had smoothly converted a large industrial firm into a many-faceted emergency relief and rescue operation for victims of the Dayton flood . . . and the real flooding had not yet even begun.

✳ 6:50 A.M.
TUESDAY

"Cripes, Sarge, look out!"

Homer Tupman whirled at patrolman Jenkins's warning and stared with disbelief at the wall of water rushing toward them.

"Levee's gone!" he shouted. "Run for it!"

They ran west in the middle of Cedar Street, the sergeant quickly taking a good lead, but they'd hardly gone a quarter of a block when the six-foot avalanche of water smashed into them, bowling them over and carrying them along nearly twice as fast as they'd been running.

They lost contact with one another and each fought desperately to save his own life in the churning maelstrom. Four blocks from where the wave had scooped them up, Tupman was tossed into the low branches of a tree and managed to get a good hold. An instant later he saw Jenkins coming along the same line he had floated and he snatched the man's hand as he too hit the tree. In a moment both of them were perched well above the water.

They climbed to the top, where cables dipped through the branches midway between two telegraph poles, and from here they swung themselves hand over hand to the first pole and then walked along the wires for four blocks before reaching dry ground where they could alight and continue their work.

"Y'know somethin', Sarge?" Jenkins panted, "this is one hell of a lousy job we've got."

✳ 6:58 A.M.
TUESDAY

There were three customers at the counter in Saettel's when Mary Schunk walked in at a couple of minutes to seven. All of them were men.

"Ah, good morning, Mary," said Ollie Saettel, beaming. "Today you are on time, eh?" His eyes twinkled merrily.

He looks like Santa Claus without whiskers when he smiles like that, Mary thought. Such a nice old man. She smiled brightly at him, closed her umbrella and shook it out the door, then reopened it and stood it in the corner to dry. She hung her coat on a rack, stuffed her head scarf in the pocket and shook her head to fluff her hair. She had long black curls that hung from the back of her head like soft glossy springs catching the light in little squiggly highlights. The customers were watching her appreciatively and Mary pretended she was unaware of this. It delighted her that after being married for six years she still attracted the attention of men.

The old man shook his head and put his hands to his ears in an exaggerated gesture. "Oh, those whistles. I was so glad when they stopped. They blew for nearly an hour. Did you talk to Eddie, Mary? Did he say why they were blowing?"

She nodded. "He called me. Said the rivers were almost to the tops of the levees and there was going to be flooding in the low spots. They're blowing them as a warning."

Saettel frowned. "Not a flood like in '66, I hope." He put a palm to his cheek and widened his eyes. "Now that was a bad flood. The water right out in front here was two feet deep and downtown it was four. It was a hard time for everyone then. I would not like to see that happen again. Such a mess."

The customers had been following the exchange with interest. One of them, a youth in his late teens suffering badly from acne, looked at Mary eagerly.

"Any chance the levees'll bust?"

"Well, I certainly *hope* not!" she answered sharply. "That would be awful."

"Yeah," the young man said enthusiastically, "yeah, it sure would, wouldn't it? Gol-lee, it sure would be something!"

"I ain't much of a swimmer," another of the men said. He was a husky individual in soiled work clothes and wearing a very dirty small-billed cap. "Fact is, I don't much cotton to water a-tall. Far's I'm concerned, it k'n jest stay in the river where it ort'a be."

[65]

His companion took a big bite from a fresh doughnut and nodded his head in agreement.

"I don't think it'll flood much," Saettel said to no one in particular. "In '66 — I was a young man then — it rained much harder here than it has this time. Much harder." He peered out of the big window and thought about that flood of 47 years past. His cousin had contracted pneumonia because of it and died in four days. It had been a sad time, and he thought of things he hadn't brought to mind for years. The thoughts caused his eyes to burn and a lump to form in his throat. Behind him he heard Mary making a new pot of coffee and was about to return to the counter when three automobiles in a row rattled past traveling quite fast. In the first there were only two men, but the second and third were filled with people, and men were hanging onto the running boards on both sides of each.

"Huh!" Saettel, wiping his hands on his apron, opened the door and watched the cars go up Fairgrounds Hill and disappear over the top heading toward NCR. "Huh!" he repeated. "Now that is a very funny thing."

Another car came by, equally crowded, and this time followed by a horse-drawn wagon at a full gallop. He turned and looked toward downtown and saw two more wagons approaching and a man in a business suit incongruously riding bareback on a horse. He shouted at Ollie Saettel, slowing only a little and pointing back toward downtown, before continuing toward the hill.

Three blocks north, where the canal went past just before the downtown district, Saettel could see a sea of water across the street. It looked as if the canal might be leaving its banks. He watched a horse pulling a buggy gingerly crossing the canal bridge, and the water was just to the tops of the horse's hooves. The proprietor re-entered his shop.

"People," he said seriously, "I am afraid we may get a little wet. The water is coming down Main Street toward us. The man on horseback told me that the levee has broken just east of Main on Monument Avenue."

"Hey!" cried the pimpled youth. "You mean it? It's really busted? Gol-lee, wish I could'a seen it." He leaped up and ran to the door to look out. There was disappointment in his face when he came back. "Hardly even covering the street up that way," he grumbled. "Not even up on the sidewalks. It'd have to go up a whole foot or more, prob'ly, before it even reached here. Well, one thing anyways, I guess I won't have to go to work today. You can give me another cup of coffee." He squeezed a pimple on his chin and wiped his fingers on his trousers. "Guess you can give me a couple more of them sugar doughnuts, too."

Ollie Saettel looked at the young man and shook his head sadly. He filled the cup and put two more doughnuts on the plate. He had just had a premonition — a decidedly unpleasant one — of his own.

"I think," he said slowly, "you will see much more water than you want to see." He shook his head again and spoke more to himself than to anyone present. "Much more water."

✳ 7:00 A.M.
TUESDAY

It was precisely at this moment that the river gauge reached twenty-four feet and the muddy waters began sliding over the downtown levee and into Monument Avenue just a few dozen yards east of the Main Street bridge. Hundreds of spectators watched as if transfixed as the water flowed over the levee top and down the slope. They shouldn't have been taken by surprise but they were. One moment they were watching a drifting boat coming toward them with a man in it waving for help and the next moment the city was flooding. It was just too staggering a fact to register immediately. One man standing close to the overflow spot put his foot sideways across the flow, as if this might stop it, then drew it back embarrassedly.

In fifteen seconds the trickle became a stream and the stream a torrent pulling along with it the turf and gravel, ·mud and stones of which the levee was constructed, and then a woman screamed piercingly. It broke the spell.

"The levee's bustin'!" a man shouted hoarsely.

There followed then an almost slapstick exodus. Men, women and children ran, slid and tumbled down the levee, jumped into buggies or autos or onto horses or ran as fast as their legs could carry them south on Jefferson and Main Streets. Some leaped onto and clung desperately to the sides of wagons and autos pulling away.

The runners led for a moment, the lithe youngsters and men in the van, followed by women dragging children. No one showed any concern about anything except getting himself away. The horsemen and buggies and autos soon caught up to the runners, nudging them gently out of the way at first and then bowling them over deliberately when they didn't respond fast enough. Dozens slipped and fell and were trampled on by others and yet, miraculously, all regained their feet and continued this frenzied run.

Almost as if confused, the water spread out and slowed at the base of the levee and then, as the gap at the top widened, began filling the streets, following the disappearing pedestrians into the heart of the downtown area, catching up with them swiftly until within minutes they were running in water over their shoetops, ankle deep, then mid-calf deep.

And now the realization that they couldn't outrun it hit them and they took to the buildings, seeking shelter in stores and shops and residences wherever they happened to be. Before ten minutes had passed, the streets were virtually devoid of life, with only an occasional distant horseman seeking higher ground.

Within forty-five minutes the water was three feet deep and was rolling abandoned autos along with the current or turning them broadside and tipping them over. It poured down the main thoroughfares toward the south to join with the canal and continue toward the bend in the river below the city. When it reached Fourth and Main Streets, where there was a great excavation for the proposed Elder and Johnston Store, the water poured over the rim like a great cataract and filled it up in a matter of minutes, then continued southward.

Tuesday: 7:15 A.M.

S EVERAL hundred yards downstream from where the
Stillwater River empties into the Great Miami River
is Steele Dam. At most times it is plainly visible — a concrete roller dam rising eleven feet from the river bed.

Now, however, except for a viciously rolling swirl of
water above where it was located, there was no indication of the dam's presence. The water level had risen
foot after foot until the dam just disappeared beneath it,
and then continued rising until it lapped at the very edge
of the high levee of the west bank, which shielded Riverdale.

At 6:50 A.M. the first trickles of water had eased over
the top, and almost immediately a relatively small crack
appeared which rapidly washed out and became a larger
split gushing water. Within five minutes it spread even
more, growing to a depth of six feet and a foot wide
with a fantastically powerful jet of water spurting
through it. More of the earth crumbled and still more,

[71]

and now, twenty-five minutes after the first water had gone over the top, a huge section of the levee was pushed out, leaving behind a gaping hole fifty feet wide and eighteen feet deep. Now it was no longer merely a leak. A monstrous volume of water poured into the residential area and followed Great Miami Boulevard southwestward toward McKinley Park where once again it would join with the main river body and thus circumvent the almost 90-degree bend in the stream bed.

The wave of murky water rushed across Main Street with a hideous swishing gurgle, tumbling garbage cans, ripping out gates and fences, shoving houses from their foundations. Down the slightly inclined boulevard it swept, past Herman Avenue and Palmer Street, where it entered McKinley Park and spread out in a vast liquid blanket.

Some of the frightened people in the windows of the homes around which the water swirled remembered now the man who had come by knocking frantically on their doors at 4 A.M., warning of an approaching flood, and they wished they had paid heed. Some merely watched with a paralysis of fear gripping them but others acted, snatched up their children and waded across the city park to the steeply rising Belmonte Hill on the other side. These were in the minority, however, and all too quickly it became too late to do even this as the water reached three feet, then four, then five within an hour.

Half a thousand people clustered on Belmonte Hill and saw the churning water in McKinley Park rise along the Lehman Street levee and cover it, joining with the main river body again and, except for the occasionally toppling trees, making it appear that McKinley Park had never been anything except a great river.

The small buildings went first — a shed here, a garage there, a doghouse or a porch — ripping away from their foundations and bobbing along at crazily canted angles on the surface, being hurled with great pressure against the strong Dayton View bridge. There were living creatures riding this torrent, too — such as the dozen forlorn chickens perched on the roof of a hen house that shot past. Enough horses went by at intervals, whinnying and screaming in terror, to have filled a large stable, only to disappear when slammed into the big bridge.

The residents on the east side of the park moved swiftly from the first floors to the second and from there out onto the roofs or into attics, and it seemed to them that the water would never stop rising.

For a long time, it didn't.

✳ 7:32 A.M.
TUESDAY

George Walter McClintock yawned, feeling the grit of weariness behind his eyes and glad his run was nearly finished. Engineer for the Cincinnati, Hamilton and Dayton Railroad, he had pulled his train out of the Dayton terminal at 11 P.M. yesterday towing twenty-eight loaded boxcars. He should have been back in Dayton three hours ago, but irksome delays in both Hamilton and Cincinnati had thrown him off schedule.

Now, pulling out of the CH&D yards in Xenia, a half-hour run from the company's loading depot in

Dayton, he felt depressed and anxious for a hot bath and bed. A big blond genial man of thirty-eight, he had been the brunt of too many jokes about late trains, and it had become a point of personal satisfaction with him to keep his own train on schedule. The persistent rain didn't help lighten his feelings and he leaned glumly on the throttle, watching the track ahead in the gloomy morning light.

Xenia wasn't ten minutes behind when a movement far ahead at the Trebein Crossing caught his eye. It was a man waving a jacket frantically at him while another man stood beside a wagon and team in the road, steadying the nervous horses. There were two metal boats in the wagon and eight others piled beside the road. McClintock applied the brakes and automatically pulled his heavy silver watch from the pocket of his blue-striped railroad coveralls. It was 7:32 A.M.

The engine gave a hissing wheeze as it stopped, and McClintock leaned from the cab window to watch the man scramble through the cinders toward him.

"What's wrong?" he called.

"Dayton's got hit by a flood!" The man was panting from his exertions. "Hit bad. Levee done busted 'bout seven o'clock an' it's gettin' worse all the time. They're gonna need boats bad an' we can't take more'n three in this rig. Got room for 'em?"

McClintock didn't waste time with unnecessary questions. "Third car back," he said. "I'll pull up so we can load them." To himself he muttered, "And I never believed in dreams before. Never."

In less than two minutes they were loading the boats

and their oars into one of the empty boxcars. McClintock and several of the train's crew gave a hand.

"I'm O'Connor," said the man who had flagged him down. "Mike O'Connor. Live in Xenia." He grunted as they lifted another of the boats into the car. "Me an' Mel Fruits here, we work for D&X Traction. Wouldn't've knowed about the flooding 'ceptin' we stopped here in Trebein for some coffee an' I called my sister in Dayton. That was just after it happened. Guess the levee's done busted in two–three places. Me an' Mel here, we remembered Otto Baughn's boat yard up the street. Tol' him about it and he said t'take all ten of 'em. We just got done luggin' 'em to the crossin' when you came."

McClintock nodded approvingly but his face was grim. His house was in a low area on Perry Street near Franklin, a few blocks from Union Station and only a block from the river levee. "Wonder if the water's reached the station yet?" He asked the question more of himself than of O'Connor.

"Prob'ly not," Mel Fruits put in. "Tracks are set pretty high. But if it's flooding as fast as Mike says, we won't have any time to waste." He turned to O'Connor. "Mike, you take the team and wagon back to Xenia. I'll ride on in with the train."

O'Connor nodded and Fruits clambered up into the cab behind McClintock. The other members of the train crew scrambled back aboard and the train was already moving before some of them made it.

In the cab, McClintock pulled the throttle all the way back and the wheels spun noisily on the tracks. In seconds they were barreling toward Dayton.

[75]

✳ 7:40 A.M.
TUESDAY

"You *can't* come in here!" the woman insisted. "I don't care what's happening out there, you can't come in!"

"Lady," the burly laborer growled, "I ain't one to get rough with no woman, but I reckon either you'll open this door and let us in right now or so help me God I'll bust it down. Now which is it gonna be?"

"You're better off out there," the woman said desperately. "Believe me, I'd be glad to let you come in but . . . well, you're just better off out there. Please go away!" She slammed the back door of the big brick house in Riverdale, leaving the men staring at one another in a mixture of confusion and anger.

"Fer Gawd's sakes," whined a small man carrying a black lunch bucket, "cain't she see th' water's a-lappin' at our asses? Where in hell does she think we k'n go?"

"Yeah," said another sourly, "what kind of a damn witch is she that she won't help save a man's life?"

"I said I was gonna bust down that door if she didn't leave us in an' I meant it," the first man grunted. He turned a shoulder and slammed into the back door. It rattled the whole frame, but the door held, and he braced himself for another jolt. This time the lock snapped and the men burst into the kitchen. The woman was not in sight.

"Ma'am," the speaker shouted. "Ma'am? We ain't gonna harm you none. We just want pertection from this flood."

[76]

There was no answer, and they walked into the front room and gazed up the stairs. Water was beginning to come in under the front door and they started up. She met them at the top and there was no fear in her eyes, only a sort of bitterness and despair. "Don't say I didn't warn you. It's on your shoulders now."

The burly laborer slapped his arm to his side in exasperation. "Lady," he said, "you sure are a hard one to understand. What're you talking about? *What's* on our shoulders now?"

She didn't answer but instead turned and walked a few steps across the upper hall and threw open a bedroom door. A man about her age lay in bed there, obviously very sick.

"What's wrong with 'im?"

"He's . . . he's sick. He . . . the doctor was here last night . . . early this morning, I mean. Just after midnight. He was supposed to send an ambulance to take Donald to the hospital."

"Yeah? I see he looks real sick. Is that why you didn't want us in here? What's he sick with, anyway?"

"The . . . the doctor said I shouldn't tell . . . shouldn't tell anyone . . . said he'd be back for him soon."

The men were obviously very worried now. The tallest individual, who hadn't spoken yet, said, "Ma'am, that doctor isn't coming back with an ambulance now. We're stuck here, all of us, until the water goes down. We've got a right to know what's wrong with him."

She lowered her eyes.

"He's . . . he's got diphtheria."

* 7:45 A.M.
TUESDAY

At the exclamation from the cook, Kirkbride joined him at the front window and was startled to see the water on the street was four or five inches deep and moving at a leisurely pace out of North St. Clair Street onto Third, then turning west toward Jefferson. A little worried now, Kirkbride waded across the street to the Johnson and Watson Company, where he was met at the door by the colored janitor, Jess. The Negro told him Mr. Johnson had not come in yet and then asked Kirkbride if he thought the water might get into the building.

"Well," Kirkbride said thoughtfully, "I suppose maybe the floor might get wet. Better give me a hand getting anything up higher that might get damaged if it does come in."

Jess bobbed his head and together they worked at lifting the cartons of new papers, the bales and boxes of other materials, up onto high shelves or tables. They still had a lot to do when a trickle of water appeared on the floor from the rear of the building and almost immediately met another coming in the front door.

"By golly, Jess," Kirkbride said, "looks like it's coming in at that. Let's hop to it. Forget the supplies for now and let's get these office records and files up to the second floor."

"Law," said Jess, his eyes widening, "y'all don't think it's gonna come in that high, does yuh?"

"Oh, I don't think so, Jess. This is just in case. Doesn't hurt to think ahead a little. Just in case," he repeated.

"Yassuh," Jess said nervously. "Jest in case."

✳ 7:46 A.M.
TUESDAY

The water tumbled down the stairs in a veritable torrent and was already up to Edward W. Hanley's knees. He looked at the levers and wheels and valves before him and knew he would have to make his decision quickly. If he turned the city's gas off now, the citizens would suffer from the lack of it. They were going to need the warmth it would provide and they would need to prepare hot food.

There was a possibility of explosion if the waters came up very high, but Hanley had been here a long time now and never had the water come up high enough to do any really serious damage. And as long as the gas fumes escaped into the swiftly running waters, there would be no danger. Later, as the waters receded and the current slowed, he could shut it off.

Still, the decision was hard to make and it wasn't until he stood waist deep in the water that he turned and waded up the stairs against the current. He would leave it on.

It was a serious mistake.

✳ 8:18 A.M.
TUESDAY

George McClintock eased the train into the Union Station yards at Sixth and Ludlow Streets with water spray-

[79]

ing out from beneath it. There was a weird sensation to
it all. With the tracks covered by a full six inches of
water rushing from north to south, it was almost as if he
were bringing a boat to dock.

He'd had to cut his speed drastically when they neared
Dayton. The crossings were choked with people fleeing
in wagons and autos and on foot, and many of the streets
already had several inches of water in them. Where the
CH&D tracks paralleled the Mad River, entering Dayton
from the northeast, the track bed was high and there
was water on both sides of it — ugly yellowish water
flecked with dirty foam. Hundreds of people were on
the track, and he had to slow down even more and blast
his whistle constantly to make them step out of the way.
In all their faces was reflected the same thing — a stunned
disbelief dissolving gradually to outright fear. Many
shouted at him to go back.

As they neared downtown the debris-choked water
bounced savagely across the tracks. McClintock knew it
wouldn't take much of that to eat away the track bed
and cause a derailment. He slowed even more but didn't
stop.

The water was much too deep for him to attempt to
pull into the siding leading to the CH&D freight yard at
Webster Street between Second and Third, so he continued moving toward the Union Station Yards, actually
glad it was necessary, because this would take him that
much nearer his home.

He was deeply moved by the sight of the waters
sweeping down toward him as he crossed St. Clair Street,
Jefferson, Main and even Ludlow Street right in front of

the station. Far up Ludlow toward First Street an upside-down wagon bumped along absurdly, and he had a crazy impulse to laugh.

Now, with his train stopped, he set the brakes and hit the steam release valve. The shriek of the liberated steam was, he thought morosely, like some anguished death cry from an injured beast.

Three tracks over, on the rails nearest the station platform, sat a five-car passenger train. Smoke still belched from the stack of the engine, and the windows were lined with faces, some pale and frightened but others merely interested or irritated over the delay. Three blocks ahead was the steel trestle over the Great Miami River, but even from here McClintock could see it was no more than two rows of girders rising above the water. Already there was a large back-up of debris lodged against the upstream side of it and someone had run a string of loaded coal cars onto the span to help hold it against the frightful current.

He felt sick at the sight of the water depth in that direction. His house — his family — was over that way, too, and it was quite low there. The water in Perry Street must be four or five feet deep already.

McClintock climbed out of the cab and stepped down into water higher than his ankles. It was bitterly cold at first, but there were more important things to think about. He cupped his mouth with his hands and bellowed for the crew to get the boats out. A half dozen railroad men sloshed over to them from the terminal. One was stationmaster Darryl Deltz.

"Boats, McClintock? You've got boats here?"

"Yes, sir," the engineer said. "Ten of them. Took 'em on at Trebein Crossing."

"Good man. The city's going to need them badly. I'll appoint ten men to start rescue operations with them. This water hasn't crested yet." The stationmaster looked over the men crowding around.

"Make that nine, Mr. Deltz," McClintock said. "I'm taking one over there." He pointed toward his home area. "They'll need help over there."

"I'll take one, too," Mel Fruits said. He didn't wait for an answer but waded to the car with the boats and threw open the door. The others followed.

Deltz seemed somewhat annoyed that the leadership in this novel crisis had somehow slipped from his grasp. He reasserted his authority as Fruits and McClintock towed their boats toward Ludlow Street, the bottoms of the crafts clanging hollowly as they bumped against the rails, the oars rattling about noisily under the seats.

"All right, men," Deltz shouted, "I want eight volunteers." He smiled smugly.

McClintock was deeply concerned. The water that had lapped to just above his ankles when he stepped from his engine was mid-calf high when he left the tracks at the Ludlow Street crossing, and the current struggled to wrench the boat from his grasp. He was struck by the eeriness of the silence, unbroken by the normal clopping of hooves, tooting of horns and chattering of pedestrians. There was an ominous feel to it all which filled him with a sense of foreboding.

With the wide expanse of Ludlow Street open before him now, McClintock stepped into his boat and fitted the oars to the locks. For a long moment before getting the boat under control he was swept sideways with the current at an alarming rate. By the time he had the bow turned into the current and had slowed his backward speed with the oars, he had passed the corner of Eaker Street, a full block south of the station. To avoid any possible obstructions near buildings and several parked automobiles — one of which, as he passed it, turned end for end by the force of the current and began to roll backwards — he stayed in the center of the open area which had been Ludlow Street. It was nearly a serious mistake.

The Franklin Street intersection where he had to turn was approached rapidly, the street sign sticking up oddly from the water. At this intersection the current split, half of it roaring in a vicious curve to go west on Franklin and the other half continuing southward on Ludlow toward the canal. A treacherous eddy was forming at the angle of the sturdy brick building on the near corner.

Almost too late McClintock started his turn and his forward speed was so great that the curve of the current could scarcely overcome the inertia he had built up. Swiftly he sped across the mouth of Franklin Street and slammed with crushing impact into the side of a frame store on the southwest corner. Had the boat been wooden it might well have been smashed. As it was, the rear of the craft hit the house, bending the metal considerably and catapulting the engineer into the air. He hit the side of the house and then miraculously bounced right back into the boat. Shaken but unhurt, it had taught him a good lesson in the art of metropolitan navigation.

He bent to the oars and now kept the boat just a few feet streetward from where the curb had to be.

For the first time he became aware of the voices. Every second story window, it seemed, had at least one person and often two or three in it. They shouted at him, screamed for help, beseeched, implored, offered him great sums and then cursed him as the current shot him past.

At Perry Street he let the turn of the current carry him neatly around the corner to the south, guiding himself expertly so that the boat neared the west side of the street as it straightened out again. He felt a surge of exultation at the way he'd handled it this time.

Here on Perry the current was not as swift as it had been on Ludlow but the water was deeper, perhaps five feet. The white picket fence in front of his house at 219 Perry was gone — needed painting anyway, he told himself with a sort of grim humor — but he felt a relaxation of his muscles as well as his fears to see the big old house still standing, even though the water had only one more step to go before it would be level with the front porch.

He steered the boat to a neat landing between the banisters of the wide front porch stairs and let the current pin the boat to the south railing. Holding it tightly, he moved the bow and stepped out onto the dry porch and then pulled the boat after him, clear of the water.

"Daddy! Daddy!" The front door burst open and twelve-year-old Ruthie raced out and flung herself into his arms. "I *told* her you'd come. I knew you would!

Grandma said you wouldn't be able to get through, but I *knew* you'd come home." She kissed him fiercely.

"Hi, Angel," he said, grinning. "You were right, weren't you? Takes more than just a little bit of water to keep me away from my favorite girl."

"George!" The woman's voice came from the doorway. "Oh, Georgie, thank God! I thought ... I ..."

McClintock's plump elderly mother bit her lip and he stepped quickly to the door and put an arm around her shoulders. He kissed her on the forehead. "Hello, Mom," he said gently. "I'm glad you're safe." He looked around worriedly. "Where's Robert?"

"He's all right, George. He went to Carrie's house yesterday afternoon to spend the night. She called this morning when all this started and I told her to keep him there where it'd be safer. I'm so glad I did. I never realized the water would get this high. What are we going to do, George?"

McClintock was much relieved to hear his sister was keeping his fourteen-year-old son there. She and her husband and their two sons lived in Upper Riverdale on ground so high that the whole of Dayton would have to be flooded before the water even reached them. At the rate this water was going up, though, even *they* might have trouble.

"Listen, now," he said, "we're going to have to work fast. Ruthie, you help Grandma start carrying everything you can possibly manage upstairs, starting with all the food we have. Is the water running?"

His mother shook her head. "Not now, but I thought

of that, George. I filled several pans, the old bucket and some jugs just before it stopped."

"Good girl. Get them upstairs first thing, too. I'll tie up the boat and then help get the heavier things up."

They worked fast, but before long the water began pouring in at both front and back door sills. The house creaked frighteningly and the water gurgled with a menacing hunger. Nonetheless, nearly everything that the three of them could manage had been taken upstairs by the time the water was a foot deep in the living room.

McClintock hurriedly ate a sandwich and drank a glass of milk while telling his mother he was going to try to help some of the neighbors, now that things were pretty well set here. There was anxiety in the older woman's eyes but she didn't try to dissuade him, asking only that he be very careful.

She followed him down the stairs as far as the water and then took his face between her hands and kissed him. "It really is just like your dream, isn't it, Georgie?"

He nodded, startled. He wished she hadn't remembered. He was doubly glad now he hadn't told her all of it. The dream he'd had on Friday night had awakened him with a cry of horror that had brought his mother running, but in the bright sunshine of Saturday they'd both been able to laugh about it and it had seemed absurd. In the dream, he told her, he had watched as Dayton was smashed by a devastating flood of water more than thirty feet deep. People had drowned by the thousands, and when a fire started downtown, it had raged unhampered and nearly the whole city had burned. But the horror of the dream, the sight that had awakened him with such a start, was when he recognized one of the floating bodies as his own. That was the part of the dream he hadn't told his mother.

"You stay upstairs with Ruthie now, Mom," he cautioned her, "and don't worry about me. I'm a good swimmer and I'll be plenty careful."

Tuesday: 8:30 A.M.

THE two-block walk from her house to the Public Library was something of a nightmare for Mary Althoff. As soon as she left the house she realized that the *Journal* hadn't just been headlining its flood warnings for the sake of sensationalism. East Second Street was running curb high with water now, and twice before reaching the canal bridge at the northeast corner of Cooper Park where the library was located she had been forced to step into water mid-calf high.

She considered going back home but knew she wouldn't. In the basement of the library were stacked the newly purchased supplies, documents, books and papers for the next six months, and every hand would be necessary to help move them to high shelves for protection in case water got in.

A horseman splashed past and yelled something to her about the levee but she couldn't make it out over the noise of his passage. In the two blocks from her house to the canal bridge, he was the only person she saw.

She was dismayed at the height of the water in the canal. It gurgled menacingly as she crossed the bridge, already lapping at the bottom of the span and dangerously close to the canal-boat tow path. If it went over that there would be no doubt about the basement flooding, and she was glad now that she hadn't gone back home.

Most of Cooper Park already had an inch to a foot of nasty muddy water over it, but the Public Library stood on a slight knoll right in the center of the park, and she was happy to see that the closest water to it was still a score of yards away. While Second Street had been void of pedestrians, Cooper Park had perhaps thirty or more people milling about or standing in small groups, apparently oblivious of their wet feet. They seemed to be hypnotized by the gradual rising of the water flowing in from the north on St. Clair Street, and Mary Althoff couldn't understand why they didn't move to higher ground.

It was with relief that she paused at the head of the library steps to remove her overshoes and dump water from them. As she was doing so, the door opened behind her and she turned to see the nervous face of Theresa Walter, supervisor of the bindery and book repairing. Miss Walter wasn't too successful in her attempt to smile.

"Why, Theresa," Mary said, "I didn't expect to see you here this early." She grimaced as she yanked off the other overshoe and poured out the water. "My shoes are just ruined!" she complained.

She entered the door and set the overshoes beside the

steam radiator to dry. As she removed her coat and hung it on the rack beside her desk, Miss Walter explained that she had been talking to some of the people outside and she was very frightened.

"One man told me that Main and Ludlow Streets both have water a couple of feet deep or more in them already, and another man told me he ran over here from Monument and Jefferson. He said the water was just gushing through a break in the levee and down into the street near Newcom Tavern." Newcom Tavern, a log cabin building, was a Dayton landmark. Built in the winter of 1798-1799, it was Dayton's oldest building. Theresa Walter continued, "I asked him specifically whether the water was just coming over the top or if the levee had actually broken, and he said it was cracked beyond any doubt and that if the water kept pouring through it the way it was, it might break all the way and the whole city would be flooded. What are we going to do, Mary?"

The librarian bit her lip and then waved to the janitor who appeared at the head of the basement steps. "Oh, Mr. Harvey," she said, "is there any water downstairs yet?"

Edward Y. Harvey shook his head as he joined them. "No, ma'am, Miss Althoff. But it don't look good. Reckon we're gonna get flooded?"

"I think we can almost bet on it. We have to get those supplies and things up onto high shelves. We may not have much time. Let's go."

The three hurried down the steps and began the job. Fortunately, the upper two shelves were nearly empty, providing plenty of room. Within fifteen minutes all of the new supplies had been shelved and now they began moving the materials from the lower shelves to the top also. It was back-breaking work, but they didn't pause. Here were public documents, newspapers, the medical collection, the children's library and books for their new branch libraries with all their catalogs. The total number represented something over twenty thousand volumes and papers.

They worked silently, each in different sections now and with all possible speed, grunting or moaning occasionally at the unaccustomed labors. Her arms loaded with books and pamphlets, Mary stopped for a moment to glance out of the window. She was horrified to see the water outside already gushing past the wall and inching up the window. The basement floor was three feet below ground level outside, and even as she wondered if the walls would keep the water in, she turned at a whisper of sound and saw it running across the floor. For the first time she sensed that they themselves might be in grave danger.

"Theresa! Mr. Harvey! Leave the basement. Water's coming in!" Her voice was loud and clear and she was surprised it didn't reflect the panic building up in her.

✳ 8:32 A.M.
TUESDAY

The water was already more than knee deep when Brigadier General George H. Wood stepped out of his front door at 121 North Main Street. He was shocked at the savagery of the current and the speed of the bits of flotsam shooting by.

The men in military uniform that he had seen helping people into buildings moments after the levee broke near Steele High School were still at work there, although the crowd had mostly dispersed. He waded toward them.

There was a severe cross current at First Street, and he nearly lost his balance as he inched across the intersection. For the first time since the water began pouring down the streets of downtown, his belief that this would be minor flooding faded.

Adjutant general of the Ohio National Guard, Wood was seldom at his home in Dayton, his duties carrying him all over the state, and he actually spent more time in Columbus headquarters than he did here. But he'd come home to be with Virginia over Easter and had planned to head for the state capital this morning. Now it seemed he wouldn't make it.

He had been calling ONG officers in the immediate Dayton area ever since Mays Dodds had contacted him five hours ago. He had ordered each to round up as many of his men as possible to help with evacuation work.

Shortly after the whistles had begun blowing he had taken a post at his front window and watched the crowds on Main Street, particularly the hundreds up near the levee, standing in clusters with their umbrellas shielding them from the rain.

With amazement and consternation he had watched the virtual stampede of humanity past his home as the water began running over the levee and flooding the streets. It had been a sickening thing to witness.

Quickly the streets had filled with water and before half an hour had passed there was over eighteen inches. That was when Wood noticed the squad of guardsmen up near the high school helping the few stranded people remaining to places of safety. These were the first ONG men he had seen and he immediatly put on his coat and left to join them.

Finally reaching the Bimm Homestead Building at the northwest corner of First and Main, Wood found it easier to walk. Apparently the ground was higher here, since the water level was shallower and the current not so swift. He continued up the block to the front of the Insco Apartments at the southwest corner of Monument and Main and hailed the squad of soldiers.

The lieutenant in charge saw him, called an order to his men, and together they waded across Main Street to the steps of the Insco where Wood awaited them.

"Sir," said the lieutenant, saluting him when the squad of nine had assembled on the stairs. "I'm Lieutenant Mills Matthews. My men and I have been trying to lend a hand to some of the persons stranded here." He looked around at the empty corner and continued, "I think we've moved everyone to safety who was left."

"Good work, Lieutenant. How bad is the levee break?"

"Well, it's hard to say, sir. It may not get any worse, but chances are it'll keep pulling away the bank until the whole thing caves in. If that happens, the water could get twelve to fifteen feet deep right here. All over downtown, in fact."

[93]

Wood nodded thoughtfully. In the few minutes they had stood on the landing the water had risen a full step, and the current was more powerful than before. The roar of it made conversation difficult, and Wood had to speak loudly to be heard.

"I think, Lieutenant, that we'd better set off down Main Street to see if anyone needs assistance. If the flood gets as bad as you think it might — and I agree with you that there's a good chance it will — this city's going to have to be put under martial law. The only high ground we might be able to reach is south of here at the Fairgrounds. It's a mile away or more, but if the water holds at this level for a while, we may be able to make it there and be better able to direct rescue operations."

"Yes, sir," Matthews replied, "but I rather doubt we'll make it with the water this fast. Couple of the men here already got ducked when the current knocked them off their feet."

"You may be right, but we'll not know for sure unless we try. Let's go. I'll lead. Join hands, wrist to wrist, in single file. Crossed some pretty bad streams in the Philippines that way."

Lieutenant Matthews nodded and they clasped wrists and started off. The water was now nearly waist deep and the current incredibly strong. They had gone no more than thirty feet from the steps when Private Don Coble, last man in line, gave a yell as he lost his footing. His grip with the next man broke and he disappeared under the surface. He came up sputtering half down the line, but couldn't gain a footing and was swept along.

General Wood lunged, grabbed the enlisted man by the arm and lost his own balance in the process and was ducked. His grip with both lieutenant and private, however, remained unbroken, and they regained their feet. Wood shook his head and indicated the high porch of a residence.

"Up there," he shouted. "Head for the porch."

They made it safely, but wet and cold and decidedly sobered by the experience, they knew that any further attempt to journey out into the water afoot was courting death.

Behind them the door to the house opened and a very short elderly man wearing a robe and overshoes appeared. His eyes were frightened, and he bobbed his head at them nervously. "You'd better come in here," he said, rubbing a hand over his shiny bald pate. "You can't go anywhere else now. I'm Dr. King. Dr. C. W. King."

Wood shook hands with him, introduced himself and Lieutenant Matthews and accepted the physician's invitation. When they had assembled in the entry hall he asked, "Is your telephone still working, sir?"

"Hasn't been for a couple of hours," King answered. "Neither are the lights, but the gas is still on. Would you and your men care for some hot coffee?"

It was the best idea any of them had heard that day.

✳ 8:35 A.M.
TUESDAY

An hour and half after the water first began spilling over the levee near Main and Monument, the water in most of the downtown streets was just over three feet deep at the shallowest points, but the fantastic current had slowed considerably and it seemed that the water might have reached its peak.

It was just about then that the inconceivable happened. A great section of levee 350 feet long and 26 feet deep at the head of Taylor Street east of the downtown district suddenly gave way and a fantastic volume of water thundered into the streets.

It spread in all directions in a high vicious wave of foaming yellow, varying from five to eight feet in depth as it smashed around corners, boomed down streets, tossed and buckled and broke autos and buggies and trollies and sheds as if they were tiny toys. Wherever the intersecting currents collided at street corners, great splashing waves spurted high into the air and fell back upon themselves with the crash of a Niagara.

The impact of these waves slashing through the city was incredible to witness. Trees and poles crashed down, houses jarred off their foundations and drifted into the streets to smash into one another and break apart in splintered sections. Everything movable was swept along in that irresistible current.

Dozens, scores, then hundreds of horses swam freely, screaming in terror, trying desperately to climb onto anything above water and mostly failing, being tossed into the sides of buildings or rammed against poles or sucked down in the great whirlpools that formed at every corner.

Streetcars were picked up, turned over and tossed like toys through show windows and the sides of residences.

One of them came to rest upside down in front of the YMCA, another in a cellar.

Immense stones were carried great distances, rolling along under the surface like gigantic bowling balls and as destructive as cannonballs. The asphalt pavements of many streets split and then began rolling up like huge bales of carpeting until they became so large that not even this great water pressure could move them farther. A tremendous bridge girder twelve inches square and seventy-five feet long, weighing over half a ton, shot along on the surface and then arrowed completely through one residence on Monument Avenue as if the house had been made of cheese, and then lodged halfway through a second.

The continuous sound of smashing glass as store fronts and residence windows shattered was particularly unnerving, and during those first few hours the streets were filled with everything imaginable that could float — grand pianos and chairs, sofas and beds, outhouses and oil tanks, wagons and timbers and poles and houses . . .

. . . And bodies.

✳ 8:45 A.M.
TUESDAY

Theresa Walter was just passing the foot of the basement steps in the Public Library when she heard Mary Althoff's cry for them to leave. Out of sight of the others, she didn't hesitate but ran up the steps and out the side door. The water in Cooper Park was up to her knees, but she surged through it desperately toward the south-

[97]

east. The canal bridge at Third Street was still clear of water, although the street on both sides was covered. She ran across the bridge and noted gratefully that the water over here was only ankle deep.

Stopping to get her breath for a moment, she leaned against a lamppost, gasping. There was a sharp pain in her side, but she noted it only fleetingly. The gurgling of the waters about her was constant, but a louder, roaring splash caused her to jerk around and she cried, "Oh!"

The great curling yellow water came gushing out of Idlewild Avenue to the north and met another of the same size bursting from East Monument Avenue. Still another, only slightly smaller, thundered across the canal from East Second Street, only a block north of her. The individual waves met at the northeast corner of Cooper Park and merged to form a long wall of water fully six feet high. Even as she watched, frozen with fear, Theresa saw four wading men swept off their feet to disappear in the boiling van of the foamy water. Two horses and their riders went down as well and even over the savage rumble of the water she heard the piercing scream of one of the animals. It served to break the spell that rooted her, and she turned and ran east on Third Street.

She had run only a dozen steps or so when ahead of her, pouring into Third Street from the intersecting streets of Madison, Sears and Webster from the north, similar and only slightly smaller waves tumbled forth and turned westward toward her.

She changed direction herself, running as fast as she could to the southeast on Wayne Avenue. Behind her she heard the wave reach the corner and looked back, fearing all was lost, but the waves continued their rush to the west on Third. Some of the water spread down Wayne Avenue, but almost immediately it began to slow because the ground was a little higher here and the path of least resistance was to the west.

She slowed her run but still kept moving southeast to the intersection of Fifth Street. She became aware now that people were calling her from windows, imploring her to go inside somewhere to safety, but she paid them no heed. Home was safety, and there was where she was going. There the ground was high and there she would be safe at last.

A man darted from a doorway of the old brick residence on the corner and ran down the steps into the water. He was a heavy, red-faced man with a handlebar moustache and this little exertion had already set him to panting.

"Come!" he said urgently, taking her arm. "I tek you to upstairs vere is safe from vater."

"No!" she jerked her arm from his grasp, and the man nearly fell. "No!" she repeated, starting to run again, "I'm going home."

The man took a few halfhearted steps to follow her east on Fifth Street, then stopped disgustedly and sloshed back to the house. On the porch he stopped and looked after her. "Vy you run avay?" he shouted. "You get drown' for sure, you schtupid voman!"

Theresa Walter paid no attention to him. From the first three intersections ahead of her — Walnut, Bainbridge and McDonough Streets — a small amount of water was running onto Fifth from the north. It flooded the street quickly, but only to a depth of a few inches. Beyond those streets Fifth Street climbed to higher ground, and far ahead she could see people on the hill watching what was happening below them. She sloshed along and became aware that other people were now leaving their homes and shops behind her and following her lead toward the higher ground.

Her throat felt raw and her heart hammered so rapidly in her chest that it frightened her, but she didn't stop again until she was clear of the water. A small crowd gathered around her asking anxious questions. It was hard to speak, and she told them haltingly of what she had witnessed, but the effort was too much, and she shook her head and pushed her way through them.

Thirty minutes after leaving the library, Theresa Walter opened the door of her own house eighteen blocks away at 128 South McClure Street. She felt weak and sick, and although she had walked the last eight blocks at a much reduced pace, her heart continued to pound dreadfully.

She dropped to the couch and lay there there for a long while regaining her breath and giving her heart a chance to slow down. At last she sat up and clasped her hands together and looked unseeingly at the ceiling.

"Oh, God," she prayed, "please save Dayton. Please, God."

✳ 8:50 A.M.
TUESDAY

"Jess," Harvey Kirkbride said, "let's give it up. At least we've got the most important stuff upstairs. We'll just have to let the rest of this go."

The Negro flashed a thankful grin. He didn't much care for this wading about in the dark Johnson and Watson Company first floor in water over their knees. "Yassuh!" he said.

They were almost to the top of the stairs when the great roaring shook the building and the downstairs windows smashed. They rushed to the front window and threw it open to see what was happening. They missed seeing the major waves but it was obvious that the water level had jumped considerably in the past few seconds. The current in front was extremely fast now.

Across the street in the window of the reel room of the Star Theater, the projectionist sat gazing complacently at the water and debris being swept along with it. His room was not as high as the second floor windows in the building, but he appeared safe enough at his perch with the water surface about six feet below him.

A riderless horse came by, occasionally finding a foothold which was lost almost as soon as gained. It snorted and rolled its eyes and was quickly floated away.

"Oh, mah Lawd," Jess moaned, his own eyes bulging in fright. "Oh, mah Lawd, Mist' Kirkbride, hit's jedgement day foh all of us."

Kirkbride didn't answer. He was looking up the street, and suddenly he stiffened. "Jess, look!"

The janitor leaned forward fearfully to follow the man's pointing finger. A young lad perhaps twelve years old, clinging to a heavy wooden beam, was swept around the corner of St. Clair onto Third Street. The eddy at the northwest corner of the intersection in front of the Burkhardt and Rotterman Drug Store caught the timber and whirled it in a half circle. It shot free and carried the boy a few feet west on Third. Pale but in control of himself, the lad managed to grab hold of a sign in front of the Finke Brothers Company, a notion store one building east of them, and clung tenaciously. The beam was yanked from his grasp and bobbed away.

Kirkbride swung a leg over the window sill, shook his head and pulled back and ran to the rear of the room where he had seen the stepladder. He brought it back and shoved it out the window, putting his arms under the little platform at the top and clenching it tightly.

Jess was leaning against the wall with his eyes closed and repeating the phrase, "Oh, mah Lawd," over and over. He gave no indication of hearing Kirkbride when the book printer told him to grasp his belt from behind and brace him. His hands were occupied, and so he lashed out with a foot and caught the janitor in the shin. The man's eyes popped open with the pain of it.

"Damn you, Jess," Kirkbride shouted, "you grab my belt and hang on tight or so help me God I'll strangle you!"

"Oh, mah Lawd," Jess murmured, but he moved behind Kirkbride and gripped his belt.

Kirkbride leaned far out and lowered the ladder until it was only a foot off the water. He turned his head and could see the boy still clinging with white-knuckled intensity to the sign sixty feet away. He hailed him.

"Boy! Hey, there, boy!" The water made so much noise he wasn't sure the youth could hear him, and he called even louder. "Listen, swing in as close as you can to the wall and let go. Hook your arm around the ladder rung as you go past and hang on. Don't try to climb up, just hang on tight and we'll pull you in. You hear?"

The boy nodded his head and swung himself toward the wall. When he let go he went underwater for an instant but then bobbed to the surface and floundered close to the wall as the current carried him along. When he shoved his arm scythe-like around the rung of the ladder the pressure became so great Kirkbride felt sure either his arms would break or Jess's grip would. Neither did.

"Okay, Jess," he shouted, "I've got him." He braced his legs against the wall. "Let go of the belt now and help me lift the ladder up."

Jess did so, and little by little they drew the ladder up and into the window. In a moment the boy was in a soggy heap on the floor. They stripped off his clothing and dried him briskly with towels from their laundry supply. As they did so, Jess gave Kirkbride a sidelong glance and grinned sheepishly.

"Ah, 'spect Ah got a li'l bit skeered there, Mist' Kirkbride. Ah don't reckon it'll happen no mo'."

Kirkbride grinned back. "That's all right, Jess," he

said. "Happens to the best of us sometimes. You're too big for me to strangle anyway."

They both laughed at that and Jess pulled a half-full pint bottle of whiskey from his hip pocket. "That there boy's a-tremblin' sumpin' turrible. 'Spect maybe a swaller er two o' this stuff'd he'p?"

"Jess, you're a gem!" He took the bottle and tilted it to the boy's mouth and forced him to swallow. It made him choke some but he kept it down, and gradually the trembling stopped.

They had no clothing to give him, so they wrung out the boy's as thoroughly as they could, and he put them back on.

"What's your name, son?" Kirkbride asked.

"Johnny. Johnny Beman."

"How'd you happen to get out there? Where do you live?"

"North Dayton," the boy replied. "Up Valley Street. I got caught on top of our garage, and when it broke up I had to swim. I'm a good swimmer, but I got awful tired. I floated over near the levee by Webster Street, but I couldn't get a hold on the bridge, and then first thing I knew the water took me over the levee and I thought sure I was a goner. Then all of a sudden that hunk of wood came along and I grabbed it and floated with it to here."

"How about your family? Where are they?"

"They were in the house. They were looking out the window at me when the garage went down." He looked worried. "Guess they must think I'm drowned. Wish I could let 'em know I ain't."

"They'll know soon enough," Kirkbride said. "Just be thankful you're safe. Water'll go down soon, and you can get back to them. You're a mighty lucky boy."

"I guess I am at that," Johnny said soberly.

✳ 8:52 A.M.
TUESDAY

Despite the fact that she had called for the others to leave the library basement, Mary Althoff delayed for a moment herself. She climbed the little foot ladder in the aisle and stuffed the books and papers she still held into an empty space on the top shelf. She almost lost her balance and fell in her haste and so she forced herself to slow down.

Returning to the floor she walked rapidly down the aisle toward the stairway at the other end of the building. At the aisle where she had last seen Theresa she paused and called the woman's name, but there was no answer. She decided her co-worker had gone to the north end of the basement, and she ran down the aisle in that direction.

Without warning a shattering roar filled the air. The windows on both north and east sides of the basement burst inward and great torrents of murky water poured in. Mary screamed and fled toward the stairs, but the water knocked her down when she was still fifteen feet away. Fortunately, it tumbled her right to them, where she caught the railing and pulled herself up.

In the passageway leading to the boiler room, Harvey was struggling to reach the stairs. Already the water was waist deep and pressing him back with terrible force. Only by pulling himself along with his hands on the bookshelves was he able at last to reach the stairs. By then the water had risen to his armpits.

Mary Althoff grabbed his hand and helped him stumble up to the first floor where both of them stood sopping and breathless. So rapidly was the water coming into the basement that they could actually see it rising in the stairwell as water rises in a basin being filled. A heavy metal-bound chest swirled by and they heard it thud several times against the ceiling before being pinned there. With great speed the water began edging up the final few steps that would take it to the first floor level.

Mary looked around her suddenly and sucked in her breath. "Theresa! She's not here. Oh, my God, Mr. Harvey, she's still down there. We've got to help her!" She attempted to step back into the bubbling water in the stairwell, but the janitor pulled her back roughly.

"If she's down there," he said grimly, "she's done for. Ain't no way on God's earth we can help her, Miss Althoff." He pointed at the water which now had only two steps to go to reach them. "C'mon, we better get out of here fast!"

Together they ran toward the front doors and the steps leading up to the quarters of the library's natural history museum on the second floor. The first floor was eight feet above outside ground level, and when they reached the door they saw immediately that any hope of escape was cut off. Already the rushing waters had climbed high up the library steps and three men were on the landing watching as all manner of drift as well as swimming horses and humans whipped past. One of them turned and saw the library workers through the glass of the big door, and he said something to the others. Then he opened the door a little and stuck his head in.

He was a tall man wearing a clean pair of coveralls and a wool mackinaw shirt and he smiled wryly at Mary Althoff and Harvey. "Mind if we come in?" he said. "My name's Hugh Warder." He didn't seem to be bothered by what was happening outside, although his companions, both middle-aged men also wearing the clothing of laborers, were obviously scared to death.

They welcomed him and his friends and for a few minutes they talked animatedly about what had happened. As Harvey began telling them about how they had been in the basement when the wave struck, Mary Althoff slumped onto a wall bench and buried her face in her hands. The sound of the big chest bumping against the ceiling came back to her and she thought of Theresa and pictured her, too, down there bumping about lifelessly. Nausea nearly overwhelmed her and for a moment she was sure she would lose the big breakfast she had eaten. Then Harvey's big rough hand patted her shoulder clumsily.

"There, there, Miss Althoff. Don't take on so. We don't know for sure Miss Walter's down there. Might be she run out before the big water hit."

His words didn't carry much conviction, but Mary nodded. Harvey was right, she knew. No matter whether she was downstairs or outside, Theresa Walter was beyond any help they might be able to give.

The front door thrust open and a young man, coatless and exhausted, stumbled in. He was hardly able to stand, and it was apparent he'd had a hard time. Water spilled over the threshold after him, and Harvey slammed the door, then stood there watching dumbfounded as the water continued to spurt in between the door and the sill.

"Mr. Harvey, look!"

The janitor spun around and saw from back by the cellar steps a large spreading pool of water. It quickly merged with the water coming in under the door.

"Everybody upstairs," Harvey said. He and Warder helped the young man who had just come in. He told them his name was Billy Denton.

At the top of the stairs the group halted, surprised to see three more men and a young woman standing at the far west side of the building looking down at the waters rolling past through the park.

"Hello," said one of the men, "I'm Robert McKenny." He wore a black bowler hat and a business suit. "Miss Tomlinson and these two gentlemen and I became marooned together on the front steps. We didn't see anyone downstairs so we thought someone might be up here. Awful, isn't it? Never saw anything like it in my life before. Just awful."

Laurie Tomlinson was glad to see Mary Althoff. A thin, hollow-cheeked blond of about eighteen, she was wet to the waist and shivering almost uncontrollably. Already it was becoming uncomfortably cool in the building now that the furnace had been flooded. Wet and cold herself, the librarian nonetheless slipped an arm about the younger woman's shoulders and smiled reassuringly at her.

"Don't worry, dear," she said, "everything will be all right. We'll be safe up here."

The men had gravitated over to the west windows and were talking together in low tones. As the two women joined them the conversation faltered and for a long time all of them stood looking out of the window, saying little. The scene below was something out of a nightmare. In nearly every upper window visible in other buildings, people stood and watched their city being destroyed. Outside, however, there was little sign of human life now. An incredible procession of objects bumped and floated by — automobiles, carriages, timbers, outbuildings and, worst of all, horses swimming everywhere, their frantic whinnies just audible through the closed windows. They struggled wildly to get up out of the water, and some made it onto steps where they stood pathetically. In at least a half dozen cases the spectators watched a door thrown open by a man up to his waist in water and the horse led upstairs to safety.

Most of the animals, however, simply swirled along with the current, to disappear around street corners or, terrible to witness, to be sucked down under the surface in the awful whirlpools. To witness such destruction and be unable to do anything to stop it was almost too much. The young woman verged on hysteria and it took combined efforts from the others to calm her.

After the passing of the initial destructive waves from the levee break, the water depth dropped a little, but it quickly began building itself up again. The sound of its passage was that of a nearby rapids and it was punctuated now and then by drifting debris smacking against the sides of the building. As the water level reached the first floor windows it shattered them one by one by hurtling floating material against them. It was a disconcerting sound, and Mary Althoff felt her nerves strung so tightly that it seemed one more crashing window would be more than she could stand.

Harvey had wandered over to the north windows, and suddenly he shouted, "My golly, here comes a man on a horse!"

The others ran over to watch with him. The horse had come surging out of East Second Street with a rather slight rider clinging stubbornly to its back. The animal's swimming was mostly directionless and limited to keeping itself afloat while the current swept it along. Occasionally its head would go under and the rider would jerk it up again with a fierce pull on the reins.

Diagonally across Cooper Park it came, passing the northwest corner of the library about thirty feet away. The rider, a young man, was obviously trying to make the horse swim toward the building, but the animal was just too exhausted. The group in the library moved from window to window, first on the north side, then on the west, following the progress of the drama.

Midway along the west side of the building and still about thirty feet out, the horse was carried toward a huge elm tree and thrust into a V-like angle of the double trunk. There it was wedged tightly, snorting loudly as it thrashed to free itself.

The youth pulled himself to the first big branch, which was only a foot out of the water, and now he tugged this way and that on the reins in an attempt to free the horse. It was to no avail. Soon both horse and rider stopped their struggles and numbly watched the water around them creep higher.

At length it reached the bottom of the branch on which the youth crouched and the horse had to lift its head almost straight up to keep its nostrils clear. Now and then the animal's head would dip with exhaustion, only to jerk upright again when the nose was covered.

The youth unfastened the bridle and reins, reached out and stroked his steed's head a few times and then climbed to another large limb ten feet higher. Here he sat with his legs astraddle the branch, wrapped the reins around the trunk and tied them about his waist.

Below him the horse suddenly gave a heartrending shriek and then its head sank beneath the surface and did not reappear. The lad buried his face in his hands, and from the library windows they could see the heaving of his shoulders.

Mary Althoff bit her lip, and the tears from her own eyes dribbled from her chin. "How is it going to end, Lord?" she whispered. "How is it going to end?"

✳ 9:56 A.M.
TUESDAY

When the waters became so swift that they tore away her grasp on the telegraph pole to which she was clinging and swept her downstream, stenographer Flossie

Lester was sure it was the end. She couldn't swim very well, but with the water only five feet deep here on Germantown Street she was occasionally able to touch bottom and keep her head above water.

She was swept two blocks with the current that was uprooting and crumbling many of the rickety old houses in Edgemont when, as she passed a moving van marooned in mid-street, a strong hand caught her arm and she was drawn to the top of the vehicle where six men had been imprisoned.

For some time she lay there gagging and coughing with the water she had swallowed, unable to speak, unable to even thank the man who had pulled her to safety or the other man who had covered her with his overcoat. She never got the opportunity.

The four horses hitched to the van snorted and shook with fear as the water rose ever higher around them. Just as Miss Lester was regaining her breath, the water pressure against the side of the van became too great and it slowly lifted on two wheels and tipped onto its side, dumping the seven into the water.

Two of the horses thrashed upside down in the water, tangled in their traces and already drowning, but the lead horses broke free. As she came to the surface, Flossie Lester's hand brushed the harness strap of one and she clutched it.

Fighting both the current and the movements of the horse, eventually she managed to straddle the animal's back, gripped its mane and clung with all the determination of a leech. Twenty minutes later the horse staggered from the water onto high ground near a farmhouse southwest of town, and Flossie Lester slumped to the ground unconscious.

She was carried to safety in the farmer's house, and when revived she looked about wildly and the first question she asked was, "Where's the horse?" They told her it was safe in the barn, whereupon she smiled wearily and said, "That's good. I want to find out who the owner is and buy it."

As it was to do with many of its other victims, the flood changed Miss Lester's outlook. Until this day she had hated all horses with a passion.

✳ 10 A.M.
TUESDAY

It had taken a great deal out of Edgar Newell to climb the telegraph pole, and he hung across the high T-bar to regain his strength. A resident of the Old Soldiers Home at the Veterans Administration Center, he was no longer the lithe youngster he had been in the Army Signal Corps or later as a reporter for the Associated Press. At seventy-four he might still be keen of mind, but he was also considerably short of wind and frail of health.

He had gone to the high-water mark in the morning after news of the flooding had reached the Home and seen for himself the disaster that was developing. He knew immediately what he'd have to do.

Now he opened his penknife and set to work, chuckling softly as he saw how the tricks he'd learned so many years ago remained with him. A few minutes later a strange message without proper identification flowed over the wires in Morse code to the New York offices of the Associated Press:

DAYTON OHIO BEING DESTROYED BY WORST FLOOD IN HISTORY STOP SEND MEN TO COVER IMMEDIATELY STOP WHOLE CITY GOING UNDER THIRTY FEET OF WATER STOP ALERT RED CROSS STOP

NEWELL

He laughed aloud as he finished the message. AP had not received a message signed NEWELL in decades. They'd have a time figuring out who he was.

A fit of coughing cut off his laughter, and he nearly lost his balance on the pole. His face was pinched and white when he was finally able to gain a deep breath. He started the next message immediately, sending it to the only federal official he knew.

FRANK W HOWELL U S COMMISSIONER WASH D C
DAYTON OHIO BEING DESTROYED BY SEVERE FLOOD STOP SEND FOOD CLOTHING FUEL BOATS MEN RELIEF STOP NOTIFY RED CROSS SOONEST STOP WHOLE CITY GOING UNDER STOP HELP NEEDED NOW REPEAT NOW

NEWELL

✳ 10:40 A.M.
TUESDAY

The six teachers from Steele High School who had been on the levee as the waters began to pour over the top fled immediately to the confines of the massive stone building. They expected to find many other refugees

[114]

inside, but apparently nearly everyone else had run half a block or more before the thought of seeking indoor safety even occurred to them. The pressing need to merely get away dominated.

"We can't tell for sure how high this water's going to get," said C. J. Schmidt, clerk for the Board of Education, looking uneasily out of the north window at the waterfall continuing to roar down the side of the levee, "but we'll have to assume that it might cover the entire first floor. I'd suggest we repair to the offices immediately and start carrying all records and files upstairs where they'll be safe."

The others — Lucia Hall, William Shantz, Corinne Borghardt, Frank Anderson and Robert Hall — agreed and immediately began the job. The main offices were cleared of their records and files first, and the material was stored on shelves in the second story office located in the turret-like tower that rose four floors from ground level at the northwest corner of the building. Next they began to save the materials in the individual classrooms and teachers' offices.

They were almost to the office of Professor August Foerste, science and physics teacher, when the rising waters forced them to forego further preservation work and get themselves safely ensconced upstairs.

Inside Foerste's office was a large wooden file in which were collected his entire project materials of charts, maps, records and data about the coastal structure of the United States. It was a massive manuscript upon which he had been working for the past twenty years.

At 10:40 A.M., the window to this office smashed and the file floated outside. In passing over the windowsill it bumped and tipped, the drawer flew open and the Foerste Coastal Harbor Project was lost forever.

✳ 10:55 A.M.
TUESDAY

Sergeant Major Ed L. Harper, battalion sergeant of the Third Regiment, Ohio National Guard, spotted the boat first as he and First Sergeant William Harris picked their way along the top of the Mad River levee a quarter mile east of the Barney and Smith Car Company.

"Bill," he said, gripping his companion's arm excitedly, "look there!"

The boat, a cumbersome, half-sunken rowboat, was jammed along the bank, caught in the branches of a large tree that had lodged there. Amazingly, the oars still rested in their oarlocks. The two soldiers ran to it and together pulled it out of the water and overturned it.

"Now we can really do some good around here, Ed," Harris said as they righted the craft and got it back into the water. "I'll take the oars first and we'll spell each other."

Harper sat in the rear seat as Harris shoved them into the current and manned the oars, but it was only with the greatest effort that Harris was able to maintain a certain degree of control and begin to approach the north bank. By then they were rapidly approaching

[116]

the partially submerged Main Street bridge. He maneuvered the boat between the Bellevue Apartments and the bridge to the head of Lehman Street, where they paused momentarily in the relatively sheltered water between a corner saloon and the residence next door.

A man's voice calling from the third floor of the Bellevue attracted their attention. He had a long rope trailing down into the water and stretched out with the current, but it had snagged on the foot spike of a telephone pole and could not be drawn in. Both soldiers were surprised when they realized they hadn't even seen it, although they had had to cross it. The man above was pointing, and though they couldn't make out his words they followed the direction of his arm and saw at the end of the rope, a hundred feet below them, a man caught by the arm and turning over and over with the current.

"Let's go!" Harper said and shoved off. They were nearly to the victim when they reached the rope, and Harper, who had crawled past Harris to the front of the boat, grabbed it and held on grimly while the boat shifted and swung with its bow toward the Bellevue.

Carefully Harper let the boat ease backwards while Harris got into the stern. As they came closer they could see that the rope had formed a half-hitch about the man's wrist and he seemed to be drowned. When they reached him, Harris shouted, "Hold it, Ed," and pulled him into the boat.

"I'll work on him," he said. "Can you pull us back?"

Harper nodded and began the difficult hand-over-hand

pull on the rope, gradually drawing the boat back to the big building. They were halfway there when Harris cried exultantly, "He's alive!"

Harper didn't answer. He was having a difficult time freeing the rope from the pole while at the same time holding the boat steady.

In the bottom of the boat the man vomited and groaned and then was sick again. He was a tiny man, scarcely five feet tall and very thin. His shoes and socks were gone, as was his coat, and his feet were blue from the cold. He was still dazed and in a state of shock when they reached the building, but it was too high to hand him up to the waiting arms.

"We'll have to tie him with the rope and you can pull him up," Harris said. "He's pretty light." The man in the window held his finger and thumb up in a circle, and while Harper held the rope in front, Harris tied the loose end of it under the flaccid arms of the little man.

"There's a fireman down there, too," the man shouted. They looked where he pointed, and saw a man perched in a tree that was growing from the top of the levee about a hundred yards downstream from where this man had been in the current.

"He was trying to get to this fellow but he lost his grip on the rope. Think you can reach him?"

"How much rope do you have?"

"No more than was out. Not enough to reach the tree."

"I was afraid of that. Well, we'll be floating free as soon as you pull this man up. We'll get to him without any trouble but it might be too much to try to buck this current coming back. Soon as you get the rope off this guy, play it out again and maybe we can reach it."

The man above waved his hand, and Harris held the semi-conscious little man as high as he could along the wall until he felt the weight taken from him. Harper had taken the oars now, and as they drifted free with the current he guided them toward the tree. Harris looked back and grinned when the little man they'd saved was drawn inside.

They were still a dozen yards above the tree when some object beneath the water caught the boat and caused such a savage jerk that Harris sailed out of the back seat into the water. Harper lost the oars and found himself half out of the boat, hanging over the gunwale. He tried to pull himself up but the boat smashed into the fireman's tree with such impact that it split in half.

Above him, when he surfaced, he heard the fireman calling, but he was already ten yards past the tree and could not swim back to it against the current. The heavy combat boots he was wearing were like lead weights on his feet, and it was all he could do to keep himself afloat.

He looked about wildly for Harris and then saw his head bobbing in the water thirty feet or more behind and perhaps a dozen yards farther out in the open current of the river. Harris saw him as well and waved briefly, then swam with the current to try to reach his comrade.

The swift waters rushed them toward the Dayton View bridge with a speed neither of them could check, but Harper felt a surge of relief. They could pull themselves out at the structure and then simply wait there to be rescued themselves. He badly underestimated the pressure of the river around him. He threw out his hands to catch the bridge, but the current thrust him into it with such force that it stunned him and he was swept beneath it. Instants later the same thing happened to Harris.

Neither man resurfaced on the other side of the bridge.

✳ 11 A.M.
TUESDAY

McKinley Park was a lake studded with rooftops and the upper stories of homes, on which and in which were crowded the residents of the area. The noise was thunderous and frightening, and yet faintly above it every now and again the people standing silently, helplessly on Belmonte Park Hill could hear the screams of the trapped, the pleas, the entreaties for aid.

Now the debris that floated by was larger and the power of the water more awe-inspiring in the manner with which it tossed these objects about. The park bandstand broke loose and floated away. Trees toppled, and a two-story frame house floated into the north end of the park, sitting upright and looking considerably like an unusually large houseboat. The remaining trees and poles in its way were snapped off as if they were toothpicks and the crowd gasped as one as the front door opened and a man in shirt sleeves looked out fearfully. Behind him stood a woman with a baby in her arms, and her face was as white, her eyes as wide and frightened as her husband's.

There were warning calls from the crowd for them to get out, to jump, to do something to get away from the house before it struck the Dayton View Bridge, but the man merely stared at the looming structure for a moment and then closed the door and the crowd fell silent, awaiting the inevitable collision.

The house bumped the top of the levee as it passed over it, canting slightly, and there were some in the crowd who swore they heard the keening, high-pitched scream of a woman inside. Just before the house struck the bridge the sharp reports of two gunshots came from inside and then there was the grinding crash as the building hit. It split from roof to foundation as it it were an egg, and as the grinding and splintering continued, the house turned turtle, its timbers snapping and spinning through the air. The floor of the house broke away intact, slid over the railing and deposited itself neatly on the roadway of the bridge. The remainder of the house was dragged beneath the surface, under the bridge, and on the other side a great armada of broken wood bits popped to the surface and whirled away.

There was no further sign of the three residents of the house.

✱ 11:30 A.M.
TUESDAY

The voice of George Burba, secretary to James M. Cox, was clear and strong on the telephone.

"Governor, there's a Miss Mabel Bardman of the Ohio

Red Cross Society on the line wanting to speak with you. She says it's urgent."

The governor sighed. People's business was always urgent. He wished just once someone could come to him with a request that wasn't urgent. "All right, George," he said wearily, "put her on. You stay on the line, too."

Burba made the connection and the governor heard him say, "Here's Governor Cox now, Miss Bardman."

"Miss Bardman," Cox said expansively, "how good of you to call. I hope there may be something I can help you with."

"Instructions are all I need, Governor Cox," she said crisply. "What do you want us to do about this flood situation in Dayton?"

There was a slight pause before Cox said carefully, "I wasn't aware that we had a flood situation in Dayton, Miss Bardman. Where, may I ask, did you get the information that it was flooding there?"

She sounded somewhat flustered that he didn't know about it already. "Why . . . why, the Associated Press called me and asked what kind of relief you were authorizing we send, if any. I must admit," she added, "that I hadn't heard anything about it until I got that call. Apparently, however, they seem to think it's pretty bad."

"How did they find out?"

"Well, as I understand it, someone in Dayton broke into regular telegram communications somehow and sent an account of what was happening to the AP in New York City, as well as to a U. S. commissioner in Washington. AP contacted their bureau here and that's when they called me."

"Well," Cox said, "I'll be quite frank, Miss Bardman. This is the first I've heard about it. Why don't you let me do a little checking and I'll get in touch with you again as soon as possible."

"All right, sir. Thank you. Mr. Burba, I believe, has my number. Good-by."

She hung up, and Cox said, "You still there, George?"

"Right here, Governor."

"See what you can find out. If Dayton's having a flood, it'll take precedence over everything else. Hop to it."

"Yes, sir."

✳ NOON
TUESDAY

Architect Harry Schenck had stood on the Belmonte Park Hill with the others and watched the continuing inundation and destruction of more than half a hundred homes. The water was still rising at an alarming rate, and as he watched the debris drift past, his heart felt near to bursting in him with pity for the marooned whose screams still came faintly, along with the constant sound of chopping as many hacked their way from attics to roofs to escape the rising water.

Less than a block away, safe from the raging waters, was his house, and in the basement of it, a small light rowboat. For two hours he had wrestled with himself over whether or not to get it, to try to save these people, knowing that to venture into that water with any kind of boat, regardless of how large, was courting total disaster.

Then, at noon, the rumor had spread, whispered at first

and then shouted in rising panic. The Lewistown Reservoir — a dam sixty-five miles north which impounded Indian Lake, the headwaters of the Great Miami River — had broken! This fierce, irresistible body of water raging below them in McKinley Park was therefore only the forerunner of what was to come when the waters of the lake got here. The whole of Dayton would be utterly destroyed. All was lost.

The crowd broke, ran, stampeded. Women snatched up their children and men gripped their wives' hands and pulled them along in a headlong, pell-mell rush to the north, to the only way away from this accursed valley.

Through it all Harry Schenck stood and watched, and now, strangely, the fear in him was gone. No one thought to ask how it could be known that the reservoir had been broken, and Schenck was no exception. But now it was as if only the *possibility* of danger was gone and the *certainty* of it remained, and so, quietly he turned and walked to his house to get his boat.

When he returned to the hill dragging the craft behind him by a rope attached to the bow, the crowds had reformed and, while no longer as large as they had been, there were still many. There was a certain calmness about them too, as if they were prepared to meet with implacability the worst the flood could throw at them.

They cheered as Schenck launched his boat, but few had any hope for him and none volunteered to help. With consummate skill, however, Schenck plied his oars, dodging debris and trees by the narrowest of margins, and miraculously he reached the first of the houses on the other side.

A frightened boy of twelve was alone here, and he took him into the boat. A hundred voices or more called to him for help, but he helped those he could as he came to them. An elderly man and woman were taken from the roof of the second house, and now Schenck had to bend with all his strength to the oars to hold the boat, even though here the houses helped deflect the current. Knowing he could not hope to row back across the open park with them, he moved north and east from house to house, seeking always the most sheltered waters.

Time after time he took people from housetops and upstairs windows and trees and carried them to the three-story brick apartment building at McPherson and Main Streets, here to let them out and go after others. The blisters on his hands from the unaccustomed laber broke and rubbed raw, and new blisters of the under-skin formed and broke, but he did not stop. For a man who seldom wielded an implement heavier than a drafting pen, it was an unusually exhausting day.

✳ 12:20 P.M.
TUESDAY

"AP's hot on our doorstep for a statement, Governor," Burba said, closing the office door behind him. "*Some-thing* must be happening over there in Dayton. No telephone or telegraph connections are getting through."

Cox grimaced. "Stall the press for awhile. Tell them we'll have a full statement very shortly. In the meantime, keep trying to raise Dayton, and if you can't get them, call Springfield or Xenia or some of the other nearby cities. Maybe they'll know what's going on."

"Yes, sir. I've already called National Guard Headquarters here and asked them to see what they could find out. They said they —"

He broke off as the phone rang and scooped it up from Cox's desk. "Governor Cox's office. May I help you?"

He listened for a long moment and his eyes grew wide. He said, "Hold on a minute," and covered the mouthpiece. "It's a call from Dayton," he told the governor. "A telephone operator there named John Bell. Says he's division plant manager for Central Union Telephone and that he's on the only functional line going out of Dayton. He wants to talk to you."

Cox reached for the phone. "And I want to talk with him," he said. "Get on the other line, George." He waited until he heard the click of the outer office phone being raised and then said, "Hello, Mr. Bell, this is Governor Cox. What's going on there in Dayton?"

The voice that came over the phone was high pitched and charged with emotion. "It's bad, Governor," Bell said. "Awful bad. The whole city's going under water. Dayton's being washed away!"

"Easy, now," Cox soothed, "easy. Tell me what happened."

"The rivers, sir. They went over the levees in a number of places. I guess the levees got weak and broke then. It was like a tidal wave. Anyway, the whole city's flooded. Our office here is at 18 North Ludlow — that's just over a block from the main downtown intersection — and already there's eleven or twelve feet of water out front. Horses, cars, people, everything being swept away. It's awful. We need help."

"You'll get it," Cox said brusquely. "Now listen, I'm going to have to get things moving here, but I don't want you to break this connection, understand? Not for any reason. We might not be able to get through again. Keep it open at all costs. I'll be back to you now and then to ask for further reports. Can you do that?"

A note of pride came into Bell's voice. "Yes, sir," he said. "Yes, sir, I can. I'll keep the line open. I'll be right here as long as I can. We're on the third floor here, and the water's still a good ways below our window. It's rising very fast, so we may get forced out, but I'll stay here as long as I can."

"Good man. I'll be in touch with you soon."

He lay the phone down and waited for George Burba to come in with his pad, which he did in a moment. For a short while the governor was silent, and then he looked at Burba and his voice was shocked. "He's on the third floor and yet he thinks they may get forced out by the water. Where in the name of God could so much water have come from?"

Cox had asked the question of himself, and so Burba said nothing. A moment later the governor began enumerating the immediate relief steps to be taken, the organizations to be contacted, the statement to be given to the press.

It was the beginning of one of the busiest weeks any governor of Ohio had ever had.

Tuesday: I P.M.

GEORGE MC CLINTOCK had rescued nearly fifty people on his side of the street in that single block of Perry between Franklin and Washington Streets. He was frightfully tired but didn't even consider stopping. There were still too many who needed help.

He paid little attention to the people who had called to him from the larger two-story houses. They'd be safe in the second floor for awhile, anyway, and he'd told them just that. It was the people in the little houses in the middle of the block — mostly women and children — that he was most concerned about. The lampposts in Perry Street no longer showed their globes above the murky water, indicating it was at least thirteen feet deep here and still rising. The terrible current he'd had to fight between Union Station and his own house was as nothing compared to the boiling rapids he fought in Perry Street now.

Most of those he rescued he merely took to the closest

safe building and let them out again. Already he had
deposited over twenty in his own house, of which all
but three were women or children. Two of these three
were elderly men, one of them a cripple unable to walk.
The only healthy man was Willard Samuels, who lived
in a small house five doors down from McClintock. A
cook in the Moon Cafe on Second Street, he hadn't gone
to work this morning because of a cold.

It was at 1 P.M., as the engineer unloaded two more
women on his own porch roof and helped them enter
the upper bedroom window, that his mother pointed
out the peril of Mrs. Stanton, a large colored lady who
lived with her nine children in the single-story shedlike
house a little way south on the other side of Perry Street.
The woman had managed to chop a hole through the
roof from the inside, and now she and the children were
crouched in a forlorn cluster on the roof with the water
less than four feet away from them on all sides.

The oldest boy, thirteen-year-old Willie, and his mother
were the only ones of the group who were not crying.
Mrs. Stanton had her eyes closed and her hands clasped
against her huge bosom, her face upturned.

McClintock had told himself he wasn't going to attempt crossing the street, but now he just nodded grimly
and climbed back into the boat, wincing as he gripped the
oars with raw and painful hands. He studied the situation carefully. There was only one way in which he
might safely negotiate the journey across. Slowly, clinging as closely as possible to the buildings on the west
side of the street, he rowed upstream until the current
became impossible for him to buck any farther, and then

he thrust out toward the middle, bending to the oars with all his strength. He managed to get across by the time he was only two houses below the marooned family. Maneuvering the boat close to the buildings again, he found some comparatively calm water between Mrs. Stanton's place and the house next door. The woman's eyes were still closed and her lips moved silently.

"I've come to help, Mrs. Stanton," he said loudly. "I'll take you and the children over to my house. We have food and water there."

"Lord's done answered mah prayers, Mist' McClintock," she said, looking at him calmly.

It was obvious that not all of them could be taken at once, so they planned two trips — the first with Willie and the six youngest children, including a tiny baby, and the second with Mrs. Stanton and the other two. Willie crouched in the back seat with the baby, and the others, all girls but the baby, lay in the bottom of the boat at McClintock's instructions, two in the front, two in the middle, and one between the man and the older boy.

It was harder rowing with the additional weight, but the current on the east side of the street was not as great, and as they neared the upstream corner there was even a back-eddy which helped them along. Two houses from the corner McClintock headed the boat out into the current again, and even though it was an easier crossing in this direction, it took much effort to cover the distance across the street before they were carried down to the Washington Street intersection. Close to the buildings again on his own side of the street, he gradually moved the boat back to his own house. His mother and one of the men he'd dropped off there came out on the porch roof and helped unload the children.

All of them had stopped crying now, but after the girls had climbed to safety and Willie had handed out the infant boy to Mrs. McClintock and then scrambled out himself, his own chin began trembling.

"Git mah mamma, Mist' McClintock," he begged. "Please git mah mamma. She cain't swim. She cain't swim like nothin'."

"I'll get her, son," the engineer said softly. "Don't you worry now. I'll have her back over here in just a little while."

He pushed off and once again rowed strenuously against the current toward Franklin Street. Within twenty minutes he was back at his own house again with Mrs. Stanton and the last two children, a boy and a girl.

He helped them into the house after tying the boat with a long rope to the leg of the bed inside the house. His shoulders ached with a weariness they had never before known and he thought longingly of that hot bath he had anticipated on the run back to Dayton. He would have given much to have it now. He was more than surprised when his mother handed him a large mug of hot broth. He stared at it dumbly.

"Drink it down, Georgie," Mrs. McClintock said. "You'll feel better. It'll strengthen you."

"How in the blazes did you work this miracle?" he asked her. The heat of it and the aroma almost made him dizzy.

The older woman grinned. "Nobody's going to be taking a bath for a good while," she said. "Mr. Samuels here broke up a couple of dresser drawers for me and a chair and we built a little fire in the tub. He heated it there. It was the only place."

✳ 1:30 P.M.
TUESDAY

Nothing had ever looked so good to Earl Hunt of 918 West Third Street than the fire department boat which hove into view a block up the street and quickly drifted toward them.

"I told you, Emma," he said gleefully. "I *knew* someone would come for us. I just knew it."

He leaned from the window and waved his arms to attract the attention of the approaching fireman, who nodded and guided the boat as best he could to the second-floor window of the flimsy frame dwelling.

They had been praying for rescue as the waters rose ever higher, but now that it was here, Emma Hunt became afraid. At thirty-two she was short and fat and had never learned to swim. She even disliked wading because all her life she had been plagued by a fear of free waters. Even when taking the streetcar downtown she used to cross her fingers as the trolley rattled across the big bridge over the river, and once, when she had decided to walk home, she had paused in the middle of the bridge and looked down at the water and had been filled with an almost uncontrollable desire to climb the rail and let herself drop. It had always been that way — a sort of hypnotic influence which never failed to leave her deeply shaken.

Now the boat bumped against the side of the house and Hunt gripped hands with the fireman, Ernest Doudna. "Oh, you don't know what a wonderful sight you are, you sure don't. You gonna take us someplace safe, aren't you?"

"Going to try," Doudna answered, nodding his helmeted head. "This current's pure hell, though." He saw Emma Hunt behind her husband and added, " 'Scuse me, ma'am. Didn't see you there."

Hunt was well aware of the water's power. The house had been creaking and groaning in the most frightening way ever since the water had covered the first floor, and several times there had been the sharp poppings of timbers snapping. He was sure the place couldn't last much longer.

"C'mon, Emma," he said, "we'll help you in. We've got to get out of here."

"Can't we stay, Earl?" she asked in a small, frightened voice. "Supposing we turn over out there. What'd happen then?"

"Em," he said sharply, "we *gotta* go. This ol' house just won't last much longer. This man here knows his business. He won't let us get turned over," he turned to Doudna, "will you?"

"Look," Doudna said in an exasperated tone, "there's lots of people to help. If you want to come along with me, fine, and if you want to stay here, that's fine too. But there's no time to stand around talking about it. Which is it going to be?"

"We'll go, we'll go!" Hunt said hurriedly. "Emma! Take

my hand now and I'll help you out. Come *on!*" It was an order now, not a request.

Hesitantly, Emma Hunt took her husband's hand and with some difficulty sat on the windowsill and swung her legs outside. The boat was four feet below and she reached for Doudna's free hand. At that instant a floating telephone pole struck the bow of the boat, jolting it badly. She missed the fireman's hand and began to fall. Immediately Hunt released his grip on Doudna's wrist and lunged to grab his wife, but she slipped away and fell heavily into the rear of the boat.

Doudna's balance had been precarious enough when he had Hunt's hand to help steady him, but the sharp tilting of the boat as the woman fell into it made him lose even that, and he pitched into the water. He came up quickly beside the drifting boat, which was rapidly picking up speed, and reached for it but missed. His boots and coat weighted him down severely, and before they reached the corner of Williams Street, he had disappeared.

Emma Hunt heard her husband's anguished scream as she drifted away, and then there was only the spinning of the boat and the terrible gurgling of the water. The boat shot past Williams Street and continued a block west to Broadway, where it was caught in a huge whirlpool and held, turning round and round for fully three minutes before being shot away downstream, south on Broadway.

Less than one hundred feet from the whirlpool, the boat smashed broadside into a pole, split and sank immediately. Emma Hunt did not even come to the surface once. She was dead before the current had pulled her to Fifth Street, but her journey was far from over.

The current here was phenomenally strong, and it towed her limp body with no more effort than if it had been a straw. Past Home Avenue she was drawn and then past Germantown Street and Bolander and Miami Chapel Road. As the body neared Nicholas Road it angled to the southwest with the current, skirting the Broadway bridge and finally tumbling free with considerable speed in the main bed of the Great Miami River as it left town.

During the next five miles the body of Emma Hunt alternated between bumping along the bottom of the river to lazily rolling near the surface. A slight bend in the river just before it reached Miamisburg caused it to drift out of the main stream bed and over inundated farm land. Here it sunk again and caught on the submerged barbed wire fence of the Nichols cattle farm. The wires pulled loose from the fence posts at first, wrapping about her body as if they were the tentacles of some weird octopus, but eventually they snubbed tightly against other fences and the last long journey of Emma Hunt had ended — eleven feet below the water's surface and six miles from her home.

It would be weeks before the body was found, and even then the encasing strands of wire would have to be snipped away with shears to free her. She was only the first of many who drowned to be swept far from the city of Dayton.

✳ 1:40 P.M.
TUESDAY

The water on the first floor of the library was now nearly five feet deep, indicating there was no less than thirteen feet of water in Cooper Park. Because of the grayness of the sky outside and the fact that they had no electric light, it was very dim down there, but from the window at the landing of the stairs Mary Althoff and the library janitor looked at the continuing destruction of the book stack, delivery and reference room.

Every now and again another bookcase would topple or shelves would fall, dropping their volumes into the water. The surface carried an incredible litter of floating objects — mostly books and papers, but also desks and tables, chairs, shelves, empty book trays, catalogs and carts and file boxes.

How calmly I look at all this, Mary thought. These books, these materials are my work, my life, and yet I can see them being destroyed and I feel nothing but a strange numbness. I know Theresa Walter must still be down there in the basement and yet I won't let myself believe it. So much easier to tell myself that somehow she got away. Is this how man has managed to survive the disasters he has lived through — by refusing to accept what he knows has happened or is happening and looking instead to the future?

"Terrible havoc down there, Miss Althoff."

Harvey's words cut off her thoughts and she patted the man's arm, showing a tight strained smile. "It's bad," she agreed, "but we're safe upstairs and we'll be all right and we'll have a good library again. You'll see."

"Yes'm," the janitor said. He looked at her respectfully and then took her elbow. "Nothin' we can do here, I reckon. Guess we oughta get back up to the museum with the others."

The librarian nodded and they mounted the stairs together. The museum was a hodge-podge collection of artifacts and fossils, early American antiques, mounted insects and birds and mammals. There were dozens of large glass cases displaying numerous objects of dusty antiquity, and from the ceiling hung mounted eagles on the wing and wired skeletons of strange beasts, a dilapidated Indian canoe, war drums and old hornet nests. On the walls were stretched hides of zebras and buffalo and leopards, the tired heads of dozens of animals that had breathed their last a score of years ago or more and destined to an eternity of glass-eyed stares at curious museum goers.

Through the years the collection had grown, until now there was scarcely room for it here on the second floor of the library building, and there had been tentative plans to move it somewhere else in the city and use this space for the equally expanding library collection. Mary Althoff suddenly wished with a savage bitterness that the museum had been downstairs and the library up, or that the museum had already moved and the more valuable of the library's collection had been stored up here.

The men were grouped near the west wall and seemed curiously busy. The librarian and janitor walked toward them, and suddenly Mary's eyes widened.

"What are you *doing?*" she demanded.

The men looked at her in surprise. On the floor they had placed a huge three-legged iron pot and beside it on the floor was a pile of old Indian bows and arrows, spears, paddles and other wooden objects. The man in the bowler and business suit was ripping pages from a catalog and crumpling them into the pot. He grinned at her.

"No need for us to be without any heat at all," he explained. He waved his arm at the museum's collection. "Plenty of burnables here, and this old kettle will keep the fire safely contained."

"You men put those objects back where you got them," she said sternly. "Immediately! How dare you think of destroying them?"

"But, ma'am," one of the older men protested, shifting uneasily and nervously rubbing one hand with the other, "we got to have some heat. Most of us are wet an' cold an' it bein' so clammy in here, ain't none of us gonna dry less'n we have some heat."

"There will be no fires built here or elsewhere in the library building," Mary Althoff said emphatically. "Many of these pieces are wholly irreplaceable." One of the other men started to speak, but she cut him off. "Besides which, just what would happen if this building should catch on fire? A fire would not only destroy all this," she flung her hand out in a sharp gesture and her eyes were snapping, "but it would endanger all our lives. Now I'm sure I'm as wet and miserable as any of you, but there will not be a fire lighted in this building! Is that clear?"

The businessman, McKenny, shrugged. "You're boss, I

guess." He picked up an armload of Indian weapons and carried them back to where he'd gotten them. After a moment the others began to help. It was obvious that they were all very disgusted.

Everything but the big kettle was put back in place, and two of the men were lifting that when a tremendous explosion rocked the building. Two of the panes in the west windows shattered and glass sprayed all over the floor. Surprisingly, none of the group fell, although all of them staggered.

"My God," Harvey said, "what was that?"

They ran to the west windows and looked out. A great cloud of smoke and dust filled the air at the northwest corner of Third and St. Clair Streets. As it cleared they could see the remains of the Burkhardt and Rotterman Drug Store, the whole front portion collapsed into the bubbling waters, but the rear quarters still standing grotesquely.

"Good heavens," Mary said, "it blew up. Oh dear, I hope no one was in the building."

Curious, frightened heads were now poking from the windows of the business places next to the destroyed shop. Windows there were shattered and the buildings pockmarked from bits of flying rubble. Directly across St. Clair Street from the library, two women showed frightened faces at the upstairs window of a frail wooden tobacco warehouse where they had taken refuge. Smoke continued to rise from the ruins, and the same thought occurred to the members of the library group at once. If a fire broke out there would be no way to control it.

Hundreds of lives might be lost. It was frightening to even contemplate.

"Hey!"

The call came to them over the sound of the water's rumble, and they saw the young man in the tree wave an arm at them.

"Hey, there, in the library. Can you throw a rope to me? I'm getting awfully cold and stiff out here." It was the first he'd said since initially calling to them that he was all right after his horse had drowned.

They called back to him and waved. Mary turned to the janitor. "Is there a rope up here anywhere, Mr. Harvey?"

He shook his head. "Don't recall ever seein' one, Miss Althoff. I'll look around, though."

Mary cupped her hands around her mouth and called to the youth. "We're looking for something now. Hang on. We'll do all we can to help you." She turned back to the other men. "Will one of you please finish knocking out the broken glass in these windows? Someone may get cut. There's a broom in the closet near the stairs. I'll get it and sweep up what glass is on the floor."

They scooped up the mess and dumped it out of the window into the water. By that time Harvey had come back and he tapped Mary Althoff on the shoulder and shook his head glumly.

She turned slowly to the window and cupped her mouth again. "Young man," she called, "I'm sorry to tell you this, but we have no rope."

It was the hardest sentence she had ever had to speak.

✳ 2:05 P.M.
TUESDAY

Immediately after the explosion and collapse of the Burkhardt and Rotterman Drug Store on the corner of Third and St. Clair, J. Harvey Kirkbride decided that they were too close to the danger area. Only the Finke Brothers building separated them from it.

"There might be more explosions," he said. "And fire. I think we'd better get up on the roof."

The porter nodded and the two men led the way up the stairs to the fourth floor, followed by little Johnny Beman. On the way, Kirkbride picked up a sixty-foot coil of rope and slung it over his shoulder. Using a stepladder, they unlocked the building hatch and crawled out onto the roof. Theirs was the first of a string of nine four-story buildings in the block, and they found that all these roofs had people on them.

The Finke Brothers Notion Store to the east was only two floors high, and five men and two women stood on its roof surveying the smoking ruins of the front half of the drug store. Kirkbride tied one end of the rope to a chimney and threw the other end down to them.

"Couple of you men come up first," he shouted, "so we'll have some manpower to raise the women."

They agreed, and two men climbed hand over hand to the edge and were helped over the top. Down below one of the men tied the rope under the arms of a woman and they hauled her up easily. The second woman, frightened at swinging like this so high, began crying on the

[142]

way up, but was pulled to safety without trouble. The remaining three men in turn grasped the rope and walked up the wall to the top.

"Any more down there?" Kirkbride asked.

"Not in our building," one man answered. He was about forty, wore thick spectacles and a shopkeeper's garb. "We saw at least half a dozen in the back end of the drug store building, though. We warned 'em they'd better come out onto the roof, but they said they'd stay inside as it would be safe now." He wagged his head disgustedly. "Said they didn't want to stand out here in the rain."

"They may wish they had," said the first woman who had been pulled up. She was young and rather pretty and her cheeks were flushed with excitement. "Have you ever in your life seen such a thing as this?" she said. "We've seen all kinds of people swept by and literally scores of horses. One man," she added, lowering her eyes and blushing a little, "went by hanging to a garage door and he didn't have a stitch of clothes on."

"Martha!" said the older woman, shocked.

"I'm sorry, Aunt Mae. But it's true! And one man got caught in a tree over there when his horse drowned. Look, you can see him in the branches." She pointed toward Cooper Park where the victim sat dejectedly in the tree.

"Hey, Mr. Kirkbride, look!" Johnny Beman was pointing down from the north side of the roof. They went over and saw, standing atop a shed twenty feet behind the Evans Drug Supply House next door west, a man, woman and boy. The peak of the roof was no more than three feet out of the water.

"This building's beginning to break apart," the man called. "Can you get us up there somehow?"

Kirkbride assured him they could, pulled the rope up and retied it, then tossed it down to the man, who caught it deftly. He tied it firmly under his wife's arms. The men above gripped the line and signaled they were ready. To keep her from getting wet, the man lifted her by the hips as high as he could, and the rope was drawn snug again. Then he let her go. Instead of trying to catch herself, however, she let herself slam into the wall with bruising impact and moaned in pain. Slowly she was hauled up and helped over the edge. She had a large bump on the side of her head, and her right side was sore.

The man and his fourteen-year-old son were next, and they swung themselves into the wall feet first and made the journey to the roof without mishap. The man knelt beside his wife and gently examined her to make sure she had suffered no serious injury. He smiled, kissed her on the forehead and murmured something comforting to her. Then he turned to the group.

"You've saved our lives, I'm sure," he said. "I'll be eternally grateful. My name is Joshua Timmerle. This is my wife, Laura, and our son, Jack. I don't think we could have lasted much longer down there. What exploded? We couldn't see it, but it nearly knocked us into the water."

"The drug store on the corner," Kirkbride said. "Gas explosion, I guess. There's still some smoke coming up from the front, but it doesn't look like it's going to burn."

[144]

"Thank God for that," Timmerle said. "If a fire started now, we'd all be lost."

It was an extremely sobering observation.

✳ 3:05 P.M.
TUESDAY

Harry Schenck had deposited some forty people in the apartment house at McPherson and Main Streets, and a numbing exhaustion was creeping over him, but he could not force himself to stop. Phillip Duleigh, proprietor of the apartment house, begged him to quit, but Schenck only shook his head and mumbled that he had heard someone call from that third from the last house on Lehman Street and he had to go there.

He shoved off and disappeared around the homes. He had actually been planning to make his previous trip the last, because he realized he could not hold out much longer. Then he heard the man call, and though he couldn't make out all of what he said, it was something to the effect that he had a sick wife who needed help, and he knew he would go back.

The house was a big frame structure of three floors, two of which were now submerged. He let his boat slide along the edge of the house and gripped the window frame above him and called to the man. The latter appeared immediately.

"Thank God you came back," he said. "The house can't last much longer. The timbers are breaking and I think it'll go down before long. My wife...my wife is sick.

We've got to get her to a safe place. I'm Forrest Kuntz. I'll get her and help you get her into the boat. Give me your rope."

Schenck could do no more than nod and toss him the rope attached to the boat. Kuntz tied it tightly to something inside. It seemed an interminable time before he returned with the blanket-wrapped woman. Under her arms he had looped a sheet and tied it together behind her. She appeared to be in great pain. He set her on the windowsill with her legs outside and, gripping the sheet behind her, gently lowered her toward the boat. Schenck had just reached up to take her when she stiffened and screamed, "It's coming! Oh, help me, it's coming!"

Kuntz blanched and gasped, "The baby! She's having the baby. Do something!"

Schenck told him to hang on and reached beneath the blanket. He was shocked when his groping hands encountered the head and shoulders of a tiny infant. Even as he cupped the baby, Mrs. Kuntz stiffened with another contraction, and the rest of the infant was born right in his hands.

"Hold her," Schenck said. "The baby's here. I can't let go of it."

Kuntz's eyes were wide with fright, but he nodded. Schenck freed one hand and somehow shrugged off his coat and swaddled the tiny squalling infant in it. He lay the little bundle securely in the bow and then reached up and took the mother from Kuntz's grasp. He set her gently on the rear seat.

"Get another blanket or two," he ordered the man.

Kuntz nodded wordlessly and disappeared. Behind Schenck, Mrs. Kuntz gasped again and he turned to see her slide to the bottom of the boat with her back to the seat upon which she had been sitting.

"What is it?" he whispered, kneeling beside her. "Are you in pain?"

"No ... yes ..." the words gritted out past clenched teeth. "Help me ... there's another ... another one com——" She broke off with an agonized moan.

Unbelievingly Schenck investigated and was stunned to find another infant being born. In a moment, it too was free of the mother, who lay weak and gasping. The architect stood up with the babe cuddled in his arms just as Kuntz reappeared at the window with the blankets.

"My God, man," he objected, "you shouldn't have taken it out of your coat until I came back with the blankets."

Schenck shook his head. "Not the same one," he said. "This is a second. Twins." He took one of the blankets, wrapped the babe in it and handed it to the woman. "Any more coming?" he asked urgently and was greatly relieved when she shook her head with groggy amusement.

He took a second blanket from the father and removed the babe from his soggy coat, bundling it snugly, and this one also he handed to the mother, who smiled wanly at him.

"God bless you, sir," she whispered. "God bless you."

Schenck returned her smile and then stepped back to the bow to help Kuntz get in. The man had released the rope and held it in his hand, and Schenck held securely to the window frame with one hand as he climbed in. A moment later they were on their way back to Duleigh's apartment building.

Kuntz chattered excitedly on the way, but Schenck scarcely heard a word he said. It was as if he were in a dense fog in which the only reality was his tortured grip on the oars and the only motivation one of bucking this current and reaching the apartment house. He couldn't even remember whether the twins had been boys or girls or one of each. He was utterly exhausted when they reached their destination and eager hands helped pull them up to safety. The women in the building took charge of Mrs. Kuntz and the twins and Kuntz himself wandered off among the men in something of an emotional daze.

Phillip Duleigh led Schenck to a deep overstuffed chair and pushed him into it against the architect's will. Schenck tried to get back to his feet, but Duleigh's hands against his shoulders were too much for him.

"The boat," he said fuzzily. "Have to get back to the boat and help. Heard 'nother voice over on Floral Avenue in a big house."

Duleigh continued to hold him. "You can't," he said. "You've done enough. You'll kill yourself."

Schenck tried ineffectually to push away the restraining hands. "Got to, don't you see? Got to help them. Boat."

"I said you can't, not you shouldn't," Duleigh said firmly. "Your boat's gone. It got away and drifted off. Someone forgot to tie it."

It took a moment for the words to register with

Schenck, and when they did it was as if a ponderous weight had been lifted from his shoulders, and he no longer fought the gentle restraint. His eyes closed in abject weariness, and just before he drifted into a sound sleep he muttered, "We helped some, didn't we?"

"That you did, my brave young friend," Duleigh said. "That you did." He looked down at Schenck with open admiration and felt not at all guilty for having deliberately set the empty boat loose in the current.

A few hundred yards away at Main Street Bridge, the river gauge had just reached twenty-nine feet and held steady — cresting at eleven feet above flood stage and eight feet over the highest level the river had ever reached in Dayton's history.

✳ 3:45 P.M.
TUESDAY

As the water had risen during the morning, Ollie Saettel and Mary Schunk and their five customers — two others had come in only moments after they learned about the levee breaking — watched it with equally rising fear. Saettel had tried to allay their fears.

"Believe me," he said, "it did not rain this time as much as it did in '66, and that time the water was only two–three feet deep. There is no need for us to go out and wade through water up to our knees to get to the Fairgrounds. In a moment it will stop rising, and then it will gradually go down again. That's how it was before."

Because they all wanted desperately to believe this,

they stayed inside, and the water continued to rise. When it had come seeping at first, then gushing in through the crack at the bottom of the door, their fear had become very real and for the first time since he'd heard about the levee break, the pimpled youth lost his excitement, and his face became pale and sharp with the worry of what would happen if the water didn't stop like the old man said.

Even then they might have been able to safely wade through the nearly waist-deep water outside to Apple Street, two blocks south at the foot of Fairgrounds Hill. But a wagon had come along drawn by a terrified horse, and when its front legs slipped and it stumbled, the wagon jack-knifed behind it and overturned. The horse had screamed in fear and its thrashing had broken it loose, and it fled between two houses across the street, dragging the reins and part of the wagon tongue with it. The man scrambled to his feet and immediately pushed through the water toward the hill ahead, where a crowd had gathered.

And so the seven, unnerved to some degree by this incident and positive the water had now reached its crest, stayed on in the shop. But the cresting didn't occur, and they were driven ever higher out of the reach of the waters; first onto the chairs, then the tables, finally the counter. At noon, when the water was within an inch or two of the counter top, Saettel made the decision for the group.

"We must go up to the roof," he announced. "We do not know how much higher the water will rise, but we can't stay here. In a moment it will be over the counter, and then where will we go? Only the ceiling is higher than us now."

"Yeah, but how do we get to the roof?" one of the men asked.

"In the back room. There is a ladder to the trap-door. We can go up there."

"But we'll get wet!" objected the pimple-faced youth. "And what'll we do if the water gets as high as the roof?" His voice quavered.

Ollie Saettel shot him a scathing look. "What will you do if it gets as high as the roof and you're in here?" he asked. He looked over the group, his gaze finally settling on Mary Schunk, who sat on the counter with her legs drawn up beneath her. "It is enough," he said, "that we men must get wet. There is no need for us to make Mrs. Schunk get wet, too."

The five men stared at him silently, accusingly, blaming the old man with their eyes for the predicament they were in. Saettel shrugged. "I am not so strong as I once was," he told Mary, "but I think I am still strong enough to carry you to the ladder."

Mary started to object, but the husky laborer in dirty work clothes interrupted. "Never mind, you've made your point," he said. "Me an' Jimmy here, we'll carry 'er." He looked at the old man and grinned. "You'd probably fall with 'er an' then you'd both be soaked. Ma'am," he turned to the waitress, "you stand up."

She did so and the two men gingerly slid off the counter until they were standing in water mid-chest deep.

Their mouths formed pursed circles as the shock of the cold water hit them. The other men, including Saettel, followed them off the counter.

"You lead the way," Jimmy told the owner. "We'll follow with her. Ma'am, you stand real stiff now. Don't bend at all, jest stay real stiff."

Jimmy gripped her ankles and the husky man put his big hands on her waist from behind. "Let yourself go backward," he said, "but don't relax. Keep stiff."

Mary Schunk followed his directions and felt the hands slide up her back to her shoulders. Her muscles ached already from holding herself so unnaturally stiff. She felt her feet lifted up from the counter and then she was being carried face up over the heads of the men. It was a weird sensation.

Ollie Saettel went ahead of them to the back room and started up the ladder, explaining that he would open the trap door. He threw the square lid back on its hinges and then climbed partly back down the ladder to help Mary.

She shook her head as they put her feet on the first rung above the water and pushed her body until her hands had taken a grip. "No," she told him, "I can climb it all right. You go ahead. I'm right behind you."

Saettel bobbed his head and disappeared onto the roof. Then he came into view again and reached for her hand. It took less than five minutes for all of them to assemble on the roof. For the first time their view of the flood was unimpeded, and the extent of the waters shook them. The only area they could see not covered by water was Fairgrounds Hill, and now the water was even beginning to inch up that sharp slope.

The closest building to them was the Dayton Ice Cream Company, a large three-story brick building next door to the north, but separated from them by a span of about sixteen feet. The wall was windowless and sheer, and there was no way for them to get to safer quarters there.

Scanning the flooded areas around them they could see perhaps three hundred people. The majority of these were on Main Street where it rose out of the water to crest the hill. There were others, however, in the upper windows of residences and on roofs. Diagonally across the street in the upper windows they could see the Lindsey family, and Saettel had waved to the man standing there, asking him if he was all right. Ted Lindsey waved back and assured him they were fine, but added that he wished someone would send some boats for them. Saettel shouted they probably would as soon as it was safe for them to do so. They lapsed into silence, because the calling back and forth over the noise of the waters was too difficult.

The minutes had turned into hours and the seven on the roof were shivering with the downturn of the temperature. There was just one consolation. The rain had abated considerably and now fell only occasionally and then in a fine drizzle.

Above them, on the roof of the ice cream firm, a half dozen men looked down. One called to say they were trying to rig up some kind of sling affair on a rope to get them to the top where they'd be safer.

By 2 P.M. the water was at least eleven feet deep in the street and still rising. It was about that time that two boats ventured toward them from Fairgrounds Hill. They were strange-looking boats of raw unpainted lumber and, though unusually stable, rather cumbersome to maneuver. In less than a block they hit the savage cross current at Foraker Street. One of the boats spun about twice, struck a tree and broke apart. The man in it was thrown into the water close to the second boat and this one managed to rescue him before he was swept away. They returned to the hill and did not again venture so far from safe ground.

Up toward the canal a small house floated into view and headed down Main Street toward Saettel's. Most of the current in front of the store was swinging in a sharp arc and heading west on Stout Street to rejoin the canal a little more than a block away. When the floating house reached this point it was caught by the turning current but had too much momentum to negotiate the curve entirely. With a splintering crash it first struck a telephone pole and knocked it down and then rammed into the brick house belonging to the Lindseys. Here it lodged, swaying and groaning menacingly.

Not five minutes later a garage followed the same path and struck the wooden house. It, too, lodged and formed a large whirlpool behind it on the street side. In rapid succession all sorts of drifting material floated down Main and collided with the pile, either knocking off large chunks and continuing on its way down Stout Street or else itself becoming lodged.

It was 3:45 P.M. when the explosion came.

The five men had formed a little knot of companionship toward the rear of the roof. Saettel and Mary Schunk were closer to the front, almost directly over the doorway. Suddenly the roof beneath them burst apart with a terrible roar, and they were engulfed in a huge ball of flame.

Safer because of their distance from the actual explosion, the five men were nonetheless bowled over by the blast. A long sharp sliver of wood pierced the pimpled youth's shoulder from the rear and drove through until the front of it protruded a full six inches from his coat. The youth sat up and looked at the bloody splinter dazedly. Then he fainted.

Several of the other men had been nicked by flying debris but none badly, except that Jimmy had been struck by something small but painful in his right eye. The cafe owner and his waitress had not fared so well.

The blast had lifted both and hurled them through the air. Mary Schunk had been blown diagonally north across the street, plopping into the water at the northwest corner of Main and Stout. She was washed into a telephone pole right away and grabbed it instinctively. She tried to climb up the spokes but couldn't because her lower body would not function at all.

I'm hurt, she thought. I'm hurt very badly. I don't know what's wrong with me, but I'm hurt very badly. Oh God, I'm hurt. Don't let me die! She began to cry.

Her head burned all over, and she cupped the dirty water and put some of its coolness to her face and it helped ease the pain. Her fingers touched not skin but raw meat, the skin curled and crisped and in some areas already blistered. She touched her head and the singed hair crumbled away in her fingers.

I'm glad Eddie can't see me, she thought. Thank God my Eddie can't see me now. Oh, I'm hurt!

Ollie Saettel had not been blown so far, but he fared little better. He had landed not in the water but on a wide section of garage roof that had lodged in mid-current, held in place by downed trolley wires in front of the store. Although he was lying on his stomach, both legs were broken at the knees and bent grotesquely under him. His right arm was also broken in a compound fracture so severe the arm was nearly severed. Most of his white hair was burnt away and his face was mutilated beyond recognition. Amazingly, he was conscious, and his cries for help came clearly to those marooned in the Lindsey house and the men on the roof of the ice cream building.

Mary Schunk's voice joined his and it was a terrible anguished duet repeated over and again. "Please, *please*, oh, God, please *help me!*"

There was no possible way to help them, and even as the spectators watched, fairly shaking with pity, Mary Schunk released her grasp on the spike and disappeared beneath the water.

Ollie Saettel's pleas became weaker, and often he was quiet for long minutes as the garage roof on which he lay bobbed and pulled at the wires which held it prisoner. The raft was in such a position that nearly every floating object that came by struck it. Once in a while such a piece of drift stuck, but more often than not it merely carried away with it a section of the roof. As this continued for almost an hour it became apparent that too much of the raft was being knocked away, and it was getting lower and lower in the water with the weight of the old man's broken body.

At length a long timber struck the edge of the raft and knocked off a sizeable section. The raft began settling, and as soon as the current could get to it, Ollie Saettel's body was pushed smoothly off. He turned his head as this happened and looked mutely at the Lindsey house before he disappeared in that awful whirlpool.

Inside the Lindsey house there was a long, terrible scream followed by uncontrolled crying.

✳ 3:55 P.M.
TUESDAY

"Mr. President? This is Governor Cox of Ohio."

"Well, good to hear from you, Jim. How's everything in the Buckeye State?"

"Not good, sir. That's the reason I'm calling. One of our largest cities has been struck by a terrible flood which began at seven o'clock this morning. It's a very grave situation."

"Which city?" Woodrow Wilson asked. The casualness of his voice had disappeared.

"Dayton, sir. We've been able to maintain one open telephone line to the central phone exchange in the downtown area, and all day they've been giving us a running account of what's happening. I'm told there is now upwards of twenty to thirty feet of water in the main business district and it's still rising. The levees of four different rivers which converge there have burst. We're going to need all possible federal aid."

"What's Dayton's population, Governor?" the President asked. "Has there been any indication of loss of life or the amount of property damage involved?"

"They can only be extremely rough estimates at this time, sir," Cox said hesitantly. "Dayton has about a 130,-000 population. I'm told the death toll may run to 10 per cent. Possibly even more. Property damage is incalculable at the moment, but undoubtedly in the hundreds of millions of dollars."

The pause was so long that Cox thought he'd lost the connection, but then President Wilson spoke softly, and his voice was sad. "Do what you can to help from that end, Jim. I'll personally see to it that you get every bit of aid possible from this end."

"Thank you, Mr. President. We're going to need it."

✳ 4 P.M.
TUESDAY

By mid-afternoon, all that could be accomplished was done at the Union Station. Shortly after McClintock had left with his boat, two more passenger trains had crept in and nearly four hundred people had been moved into Number 25, the train nearest the station. The refugees were not safe there for long, and soon the coaches of that train were half filled with muddy water. Women and children, old men and young, waded about confusedly, trying to hold onto hat racks and bell cords. Some of the women were pregnant and others carried babies. The crew of the train crawled out of the cars onto the umbrella shed of the Union Station ramp. As soon as possible they threw ropes to the passengers and dragged them out of the windows, through the water and up to the top of the shed. From there they climbed to the second floor of the depot, but even here they were not safe for long, and as the water began covering this floor, they streamed upstairs to the narrow confines of the tower.

Now, at 4 P.M., the water level on the columns of the peristyle at the approach to Ludlow Street showed the water to be exactly eighteen feet, eight inches deep.

The sum total of nourishment available to the over four hundred trapped people here amounted to one small box of chocolate creams.

✳ 4:20 P.M.
TUESDAY

Edward Waterhouse, night watchman for the Louis Traxler Company, stretched the ladder from a window of his own building on Main Street just south of Third to one in the Leonard Building.

"Better get over here fast as you can, boys," he called. "Walls are cracking pretty bad and she won't hold up much longer."

Otto Moosbrugger, owner of the downstairs cafe and saloon, and Gerald Marcus, of the Grand Leader Store, shouted to Waterhouse that their group would be right over. Slowly, carefully, with the building behind them trembling at the water pressure, they came across — first

Moosbrugger and three of his employees, followed by twenty people who had taken refuge in his cafe, and then the four young men who worked for Marcus, followed by their employer.

Waterhouse pulled the ladder back into the Traxler Building, and it was as if he had pulled away the single supporting prop of the whole four-story building just vacated. With a wrenching rumble it simply disintegrated into a pile of rubble projecting from the foaming muddy surface.

✳ 4:30 P.M.
TUESDAY

"I've been informed that there is grave danger of the Lewistown Reservoir breaking soon," James Cox told his secretary. "If it goes, it'll double Dayton's present flooding. I want a first rate crew dispatched immediately to the reservoir to shore it up. Prevent its breaking at all costs. If it become absolutely necessary, have them open the tailgates at intervals to relieve the pressure, but only if it's absolutely imperative to save the dam."

Burba nodded, and the governor of Ohio continued. "I don't want to be too optimistic, but I'm hoping our Dayton telephone operator — John Bell, is it? — has overdrawn the situation somewhat. People in tight situations are liable to do this. I want you, George, to leave for Dayton by car this evening and get word back to me as soon as possible, accurately apprising me of the overall situation there."

If George Burba was surprised or dismayed at the

order sending him to the disaster area while it was still undoubtedly in a very dangerous condition, he didn't show it. He merely nodded again and said, "Yes, sir. Is that all?"

"That's all for now."

The secretary had almost reached the door when the state's chief executive stopped him. "George."

"Yes, sir?" He turned and looked at his boss, and Cox smiled.

"Be careful, George," he said. "Good men are hard to find. I'd hate to lose my right hand."

George Burba colored under the praise, smiled somewhat self-consciously and departed.

✳ 4:40 P.M.
TUESDAY

George McClintock awoke from his thirty-minute nap with the lingering sound of a crash in his ears. He leaped up from the pallet upon which he'd been sleeping in the corner of the room and found the front window crowded. Alarmed at the ache which seemed to be pulling at every muscle of his body, he hobbled over and joined them. The flooding had increased no more, and for that he gave silent thanks. The water level was now only a step and a half below their floor level in the stairway, indicating close to twenty feet of water in the street.

Little Willard Samuels explained what had happened. He had been sitting at the window, staring out at the flood, as dozens of other people were doing from second or third floor windows in the block, when a small house whirled around the corner from Franklin Street. Too big to make the curve with the current, it had slammed into the brick building on the southwest corner. There it had stuck, lodged between the house and a telephone pole at the curb as pieces of siding and timbers broke off and were whisked away in the seething cauldron that was Perry Street.

That wasn't the worst of it. Four men and a woman were on the roof, straddling the peak. There was no way for them to get on the pole, as the eave of the house had lodged against it and there was a space of five or six feet of water between the dry part of the roof and where the pole projected from the water. Where the roof was crushed against the side of the building, it was a sheer brick wall with the nearest window fifteen feet away and no one in the building to help.

McClintock climbed out onto the porch roof and found he was standing in water over his shoe tops. The boat, still tied to the bed, bobbed lightly against the wall of the house. He pulled it to him.

"I'll go with you, Mac," said Samuels. "You'll need help."

"No room," McClintock said. "Boat can't hold more than six adults. Shouldn't hold more than four. And that house is breaking up. There may not be time for two trips. I'll make it all right, Will, but thanks. You can untie the rope if you want."

Samuels did so and McClintock once more started up-current. The raw blisters of his hands that had dried as he slept now cracked open with renewed smarting. The muscular pains eased, however, once he began exerting himself again. This time it was not quite so hard rowing up his side of the street toward Franklin. The house deflected much of the current, and though occasional boards from it thumped the boat in passage, he managed to reach the scene safely.

"George! I thought it was you." The woman was very obviously relieved to see him. It was Bessie Moxie, clerk in the CH&D yard office. He'd never known her any better than to say good morning to as he passed her desk now and then before starting on his run. God, but that seemed like a hundred years ago. He greeted her warmly now and then looked over the others. Two of the men were quite elderly and one an anemic looking youth of about nineteen, apparently very much afraid and trying hard not to show it.

He knew none of the men, but all were overjoyed to see him and his boat. "Thought we were goners for sure!" said the fourth man, a stocky man about his size wearing a black suit. "Well, let's get the lady in first."

McClintock snubbed the rope around a sprung beam at the point of the eave and reached up to help Bessie down. A piercing, inarticulate shriek froze them all in place, and they turned to see a colored man, nude except for an undershirt, stretched out on his stomach on a stable door as it came sweeping around the corner. He was facing toward them and screeched again as he passed, his eyeballs bulging in terror.

The current took him past only a dozen feet away, and it looked for a moment as if he would curve right into the row of houses on their side of the street, where he might stand a chance of reaching safety. The rebounding of the water from the fronts of these houses, however, kept him fifteen or twenty feet out. His flimsy raft headed straight for the telephone pole rising from the curb almost in front of McClintock's house.

The makeshift raft crunched into small pieces as it struck the pole and floated away as little bits of splintered wood. When the debris cleared, all that remained was the Negro, clinging anxiously to the pole spikes. Beneath the surface his feet found others of the staggered spikes and he climbed out of the water all the way up to the T-bar on which the wires were strung. There he perched forlornly, inarticulate sounds of misery issuing from his throat. He was about twelve feet over the water, higher than McClintock's bedroom window, and when he saw the faces staring up at him from the house, his cries became words.

"You in there! You folks! He'p me. Oh, Jesus, he'p me! Ah cain't hol' on no mo'. Ah's so col'. Oh, mah Jesus, Ah's gonna fall an' git drownded. He'p me ... *He'p me!*"

There was, of course, nothing they in the house could do, and the man wouldn't listen when Willard Samuels told him McClintock would be back soon with the boat to help him. His frantic cries degenerated into meaningless sounds. Meanwhile, Bessie Moxie and four men had taken seats in the boat and cast loose. McClintock was thankful he did not have to row against the current with such a load.

John Phelps, the man in the suit, sat in the center seat with McClintock and, despite the latter's objections, manned one of the oars. The young man sat in the rear seat with Bessie Moxie, while the two older men crouched on the tiny front seat, grimly gripping the sides. There was no more than a couple of inches of freeboard between the water and the top of the gunwales. Even a sharp movement might cause them to ship enough water to swamp them, and McClintock cautioned them to sit very still and not shift their weight.

They were still two houses away when the man on the pole saw them coming. Clinging to the T-bar with one arm, he waved them on with his free hand.

"Up here! Oh, sweet Jesus, *up here!*" he bawled. "Save me. Ah cain't hol' on no mo'. He'p me!" He was crying great tears as he started down the spikes.

"Stay there!" McClintock shouted. "We're too full. You'll swamp us."

"Y'all cain't *leave* me," the big man cried in horror. "Oh, mah dear Lawd Jesus, y'all gotta take me. Cain't you unnerstan' me? Ah's col' an' Ah cain't hol' on. Ah *cain't!*"

McClintock backed water with his oar preparatory to swinging to the McClintock porch. The Negro, moaning and sobbing, clung desperately to the pole six feet over the water, unhearing, uncaring when the engineer told him to hang on until he dropped off this load and then he'd be back to pick him up.

Had he been rowing alone, McClintock could have swung the boat in neatly to the porch roof, but Phelps apparently became afraid they were going to overshoot, and he dug his oar into the water in an enormous heave. Their direction changed and the middle of the boat swung toward the pole. McClintock immediately threw out a hand to act as a bumper and cushion the blow, then push them away from it. As he did so, the inconceivable happened.

The big Negro leaped from his perch to the small space in the bow of the boat in front of the two old men crouched on the front seat. Immediately the whole front end of the boat went under, and for an unbelieving moment the six in the boat sat there staring at the water swirling about their waists. Bessie Moxie screamed, and then the boat was gone and all seven were floundering in the water.

The current swept them away very quickly. For an instant McClintock caught a glimpse of his mother and Ruthie and Willard Samuels in the window, and he raised a hand at them. By then he was being swept around the corner of Washington Street toward the river.

Both of the old men had gone down almost at once and had not reappeared. Phelps managed to grasp the window ledge above a store at the corner of Washington Street and smashed the pane with his free fist. Bleeding badly, he pulled himself up and flopped out of sight inside.

The water was numbingly cold, and McClintock looked about him for something to grab, but there was nothing. Behind him in the water he saw the big Negro and the young man. Even as he watched, the former's head disappeared beneath the surface.

Bessie Moxie was a dozen yards ahead of him swimming doggedly but making no headway. At the corner of Longworth and Washington a whirlpool caught her, turned her around and tossed her against a telephone pole. Unhurt, she began pulling herself up, but then a heavy two-by-four arrowed around the same whirlpool, shot out and punched her in the center of the back as accurately as if it had been aimed. She sank with no sound.

McClintock looked back again just in time to see the young man whipped out of sight around the corner of Longworth, heading south with the current. Now the engineer was alone, and as he continued west on Washington he could see the wide expanse of open water indicating the river ahead of him.

Something nudged him, and he turned to find a floating keg had bumped into him. He locked his arms about it and held it tightly to his chest. For the first time he was able to relax a little, and he let his weary legs trail slackly in the water beneath him. He felt safer now. All he had to do was hang on and rest for a little while and then kick his way toward the nearest safety. He thought of his dream and felt a sense of triumph that the last horrible scene of it would not come true.

Then he was drawn out over the bridge, where one of the crossarms on the short bridge lights snagged his trouser leg and the force of the current ripped the keg out of his arms and dragged him beneath the surface. Frantically he tore at his straps to shed the coveralls, but his numb hands would not cooperate, and as the darkness closed over him he thought of his mother and Robert and Ruthie and he was filled with an immense sadness.

Tuesday: 5:01 P.M.

PRECISELY as John H. Patterson had foretold, the high-water mark had come to the slope of Fairgrounds Hill just above Apple Street and the day had passed rapidly for him as he stood there directing rescue operations. By noon his men at this point had brought to the hill over five hundred people marooned in their houses nearby in water waist deep or even deeper. The same rescue activities were being carried on by NCR men at the slopes of Brown Street, Wayne Avenue and Fifth Street to the east. All of those who were rescued were shuttled in trucks and wagons to the massive relief station that the National Cash Register Company had become. Even as the first of them arrived there shortly after 9 A.M., the first truckloads of provisions were also arriving from the countryside to the south.

By 10 A.M. some of the new boats built by the company's Wood Working Department were already in use. As ordered by Patterson, as soon as the boats were completed, a rescue man was assigned to each, and man and boat were carted to the high-water mark on such thoroughfares as Brown, Warren, Main, East Fifth and Wayne.

By noon the Wood Working Department was turning out the boats at the rate of two every fifteen minutes. They were strange ungainly craft with flat bottoms and square-cut bows and sterns. But they were stable boats which could stand a lot of punishment and did not easily upset. Even they, however, were no match for some of the treacherous whirlpools and eddies and cross-currents they met. Twelve of these boats were lost before 1 P.M., although through considerable good fortune not one of the men manning them was lost.

All during the day messengers and executives from the plant had come to Patterson with communications or reports or seeking instructions. They arrived on foot, on horseback, in autos or on motorcycles. He had time for them all, and his directions were concise and sure, never given hesitantly, never questioned.

NCR, he was informed, had officially become — under declaration by Mayor Phillips — the nerve center and brains, relief headquarters and operational corps for the whole of Dayton. Every hour more and more supplies were reaching the plant, along with military and police officials, doctors and nurses. By mid-afternoon NCR gave the appearance of an organization that had been in the business of emergency relief for years.

About that time Barringer had come along with a raft of questions and information. Patterson listened and commented, then directed Barringer to send word in any way possible to the New York office of NCR. Under his direct orders they were to inaugurate relief trains, the first to be sent to Dayton no later than Wednesday and the others as soon as possible after that. There should be a minimum of three of them, and they were to be filled with crucial medical, food and clothing supplies as well as volunteer workers. Contributions to the train were to be solicited and accepted, not only in New York City, but at every stop along the way.

After Barringer left, Patterson reflected on the flood's progress and promise. Thus far it was precisely as he had expected it would be, and he was sure that things were still going to get much worse before they got any better. He felt no satisfaction in the knowledge that his predictions had been borne out.

He had been hoping that in this instance, more than any other, he would have been proven wrong.

✳ 5:05 P.M.
TUESDAY

Ethel Lindsey had always been a relatively high-strung individual, and when she saw Ollie Saettel disappear beneath the water she had gone into a state of hysteria. It had taken the combined efforts of all of them — her husband, her son and daughter and son-in-law — to calm her. They, too, of course, had been very deeply shaken by what they had witnessed. The explosion across the street and the gruesome deaths of people they had known for years was an awful blow to all of them.

They had fallen into an uneasy silence as Ethel's crying had tapered off. Theodore Lindsey sat in a large armchair near the wall, his son and daughter — twenty-one-year-old Howard and twenty-four-year-old Dorothy — sat on either side of their mother on the bed and Paul Osborne, Dorothy's husband, perched on the window seat. Paul was a tall muscular and good-looking man of twenty-seven with virtually jet black hair and a self-assured manner of speech and carriage.

"How does the water level look out there now, Paul?" the elder Lindsey asked.

Osborne opened the window and leaned out to look at an electric connection that the water was just beginning to touch about three o'clock. He noted with relief that it was still clear of the water. "It's clammy cold out there, Dad," he said, "but I think we're in luck. Looks like the water's crested at last. Hasn't moved either up or down for a couple of hours now."

Theodore Lindsey visibly relaxed. "Well, that's the first good news today, isn't it?" He turned to his wife and daughter. "Dot, why don't you and Mother try to get some sleep? It's been an exhausting and very trying day. All we can do now is wait, and you both look whipped."

"I *am*," Dorothy agreed. "I think it's a good idea, Daddy. C'mon, Mum, let's you and I go into the back bedroom and lie down. I have to check on Teddy anyway. He's probably ready for his dinner." She blew a kiss to Paul and helped the attractive older woman to her feet.

As the pair left the room, Lindsey grunted meaningfully. "I know Ethel's just sick about this whole godawful business, but there's nothing can be done now except wait. Thank heavens the water has really crested. I'll tell you something I didn't want to admit in front of the womenfolks, I was getting blamed worried that it wasn't going to quit until the whole city went under. And that house smashing into ours upset me more than I wanted Ethel to know, too. Good thing ours is made of brick and that one was wooden."

He looked out of the window at the smashed house and other debris still lodged against the residence. What he saw though — and what he knew he'd be seeing for the rest of his life — was Ollie Saettel sliding silently into the water to his death. The groaning and creaking of the debris seemed to him the articulation of what he felt in his heart for the old man.

Howard stepped over to the window also and spoke over his father's shoulder. "Look at what they're doing over at Saettel's now."

The three watched the activity across the street with interest. Atop the Dayton Ice Cream Company were a dozen men, and they had fashioned a sling on a long rope and were lowering it. As it neared Saettel's roof, the burly laborer reached for it, but the span was too great, so he had to use a long broken board to snag it.

The smallest of the five men on the roof, his shoulder injured, was tied into the sling by the other four. When it was done they signaled the men above to hold tight and gently lowered him off the edge. They held him as far as they could, but there was still a strong impact when he swung into the wall of the taller building. Foot by foot the men above pulled him up, and when he neared the top, others reached for him and pulled him to safety.

Three of the remaining men were raised safely in the same manner, but when the rope was lowered the final time for the husky worker, he simply grasped it and let his feet swing into the brick wall. With unusual agility he practically walked up the wall, his feet to the bricks and his hands pulling him up the stationary rope. In a moment he, too, had disappeared over the top.

"Stout fellow," Theodore Lindsey commented.

Paul Osborne agreed. "Poor devils," he said, "they're probably half frozen after being out there in the wind and rain all day. I'm glad they didn't have to spend the night there. You know," he said, turning to the father and son, "I guess we're pretty lucky to be where we are. Like you said, all we have to do is wait."

✳ 5:15 P.M.
TUESDAY

The large old shed in back of the Cooper Medicine Company on Monument Avenue near Canal Street had never been able to keep out even the wind, and it was certainly no match for the crushing impact of the water which had struck it early that morning. Almost instantly it had begun breaking up, and before an hour had passed, all that remained of the building were a few large beams still embedded in the earth. Also remaining and undamaged was the contents of the shed — a single huge nearly empty coal oil tank a full forty feet long and twenty-five feet in diameter.

Penned in by the brick rear of the company building to the south, a heavy frame storage building to the east and a high wire fence on both north and west sides, the tank bobbed and dipped almost gaily amid the floating debris of the shed that housed it. Occasionally it would crunch into the rear of the brick building, knocking off large brick chunks and booming hollowly as with laughter for the destruction it was wreaking.

Only once or twice did back currents catch it and send it thumping into the frame building, but by 3 P.M. the whole west wall of the wooden structure had been splintered. The fence took the worst punishment as time and again the tank drifted into it, without much speed but with unrelenting pressure. It was a sturdy fence with thick metal crossbars running from post to post eight feet above ground level. These posts were discarded railroad track sections sunk deeply in the ground, and the fencing was a strong hog-wire with six-inch mesh. Well built though it was, the fence gradually succumbed to the beating it was taking. The higher the water rose, the higher were the heavy blows striking it. About one-third of the tank was underwater, and this is what delivered the most punishing blows to the fence. Shortly after noon the water covered the fence, and the driftwood that had been imprisoned in the yard and reduced to splinters by the tank had finally floated free.

By 3 P.M. the water was nearly fourteen feet deep here and only the uppermost part of the submerged fence still caught and rebuffed the underwater portion of the tank. At last even this could withstand the blows

[174]

no longer. The railroad track posts bent outward, the crossbar snapped, and at 5:15 P.M. the monstrous tank drifted free of its prison and out onto Canal Street.

The heavy flow of the current following the canal southwestward caught the tank, and gradually it picked up speed. Like some weird floating locomotive it passed Monument Avenue, still headed south. A lamppost in its way snapped like a brittle stick when the tank hit it and altered the direction in which it was floating only enough to move it directly over where the canal normally flowed.

It shot past the intersection of First Street at high speed, little affected by the flow of the water boiling westward on that thoroughfare. With crushing impact it rammed into the superstructure of the canal bridge at Second Street and demolished it.

The blow, however, momentarily halted the tank, and it turned in a slow half-circle before being caught by the Second Street current and hurled westward along the north edge of Cooper Park. It followed Second Street for half a block, during which time it snapped off four telephone poles, three more light poles and a large sycamore tree. Then it hit a residence on the north side of Second Street between Kenton and St. Clair and swept away the entire front porch.

The blow deflected its course a second time and it now shot diagonally across the street into Cooper Park. Two more trees were snapped off before it crossed St. Clair Street in the middle of the block between Second and Third and collided with the rickety tobacco warehouse on the second floor of which were marooned Alice

Winters of 28 Tecumseh Street and Katherine Fromuth of 29 Madison Street. The impact knocked both women off their feet. They had been standing in the oversized upper window and Katherine Fromuth fell across the sill, half in and half out. The booming of the metal and snapping of wood joined with the thunder of the water in a dreadful concert which drowned out the screams of the two women.

For an everlasting instant she teetered there, and then her companion snatched her dress and dragged her back to safety. Faintly through the air came the relieved cheers of the group of people in the upper windows of the library, who had fearfully been watching the progress of the juggernaut.

The tank bounded away and continued south on St. Clair. The submerged portion of it caught for an instant on the rubble of the collapsed Burkhardt and Rotterman Drug Store, and the tank moved broadside to the current and again bobbed south. As it crossed Third Street the current moving west there pushed at the end of the tank but couldn't defeat the pressure of the St. Clair Street current. Although the tank pitched and lurched in the frightening crosscurrents, the south-flowing current won, and the tank continued its meandering close to the buildings on the west side of St. Clair.

Between Third and Fourth Streets it methodically snapped off additional lampposts and telephone poles one after another, and the wires fell across the top of it, slowing it.

At the northwest corner of St. Clair and Fourth Street it screeched gratingly along the side of the Beaver Power

Building and then began to turn the corner to head west on Fourth — but at last it was stopped.

The telephone and trolley wires now snared it as a large fish is snared in a net and held it fast so that only occasionally it boomed mournfully as it bumped the side of the building.

The oil tank's odyssey was over.

✳ 5:45 P.M.
TUESDAY

The AP desk man was surprised. He cupped his hand over the mouthpiece and whispered to his colleague on rewrite. "Damn, we've called the governor often enough, but this is sure as hell the first time he's ever called us." He snatched up a pencil and pulled a pad over. "All right, Governor Cox," he said, uncovering the telephone, "we're ready for your statement."

His eyes grew round as he took down the governor's comments, but he didn't interrupt. His pencil flew across the sheets in a large scribble wholly unintelligible to anyone but himself, and after about five minutes he said, "Yes, sir, got it all. Yes, sir. We'll have it out on the wires in ten minutes, Governor. Yes, sir. Thank you, sir. Good of you to call us. Good-by."

He dropped the receiver into the hook and released a big gusty breath. Rewrite was watching him curiously.

"Wow! This is hot stuff. He's declared Dayton a major disaster area and already talked with Woodrow Wilson and got a promise of massive federal aid. You know what he says, by Christ? He says, quote, *This is the greatest emergency this country has had to face since the Civil War,* unquote. Says Dayton's under maybe thirty feet of water by now and if the Lewistown Reservoir goes, it'll be twice as bad. He's going to put the city under martial law, and he's asking relief help from the whole country with such stuff as food, medical supplies, bedding and clothing. Says it's premature to make any kind of accurate death estimate yet but off the record — now get this! — off the record he'll be surprised if it's less than five thousand. Good Christ, man, that's ten times as many as were killed in San Francisco's quake!"

✴ 6:45 P.M.
TUESDAY

It was the distant snapping of timbers that woke Paul Osborne. The room was quite dark, and the forms of Theodore Lindsey stretched out on the bed and Howard in the overstuffed chair were little more than shadows. Both were asleep.

The dimness outside was lighted only by the fire in the rear section of the ruins of Saettel's place. Part of the roof had just collapsed, and this was the sound that had awakened Paul on the window seat where he had volunteered to keep watch as the others slept. A wave of shame flushed through him at having dozed off, and now he sat up straight and watched the growing fire across the street. They were undoubtedly safe on this side, he reasoned, but there could be a lot of homes lost over there if it didn't burn itself out quickly.

[178]

Osborne wondered why the rear of the building had smoldered so long before breaking out into the flames that were now devouring it. Fortunately, the building was surrounded by water. The ice cream company, sixteen feet away, was closest to it, but the windowless brick wall facing Saettel's made it relatively safe.

Another splintering crash came and a whole section of the roof leaned far over and toppled into the water with a splash. Much of the fire went out but the part that had not gone under kept burning. As this section floated away from the building, a dawning horror touched Osborne.

"Dad. Howard. Better get up!"

He didn't look around but heard the pair behind him rise and join him at the window.

"Look," he said, pointing. "It just broke off Saettel's and it's starting this way."

"Nothing to worry about," the elder Lindsey said, brushing his mussed gray hair back with one hand. "Most of the current's turning right around the corner and going down Stout Street now."

Osborne said nothing, but he wasn't so sure. The debris pile still stuck out far into that current, and if the roof lodged there, it might set the whole business on fire. Surreptitiously he crossed the fingers on his right hand.

The raft of burning material paused at the corner of Main and Vine almost as if trying to decide which way to go. A good bit of the Vine Street current — more than was readily apparent from the Lindsey window — still raced south on Main toward Apple, but the greater portion of it surged a dozen or so feet north on Main to join the water still rushing down Main from the north, which was turning west on Stout Street. The burning material swung ponderously around, turned north and was caught by the stronger current.

Instead of clearing the debris, however, it crashed into it solidly and clung there. Within a few minutes the section of stable it had collided with was afire and the blaze was picking up momentum as it spread toward the Lindsey house.

"Get your mother and sister up right away, Howard," the older man said crisply. "Tell them to dress themselves and Teddy in the warmest clothes they have. Don't panic them, but make sure they hurry."

Howard nodded and vanished toward the rear bedroom. Lindsey looked at his son-in-law. "Any ideas, Paul?"

Paul considered for a moment and then spoke slowly. "Well, we should be able to make it to the third house down from here — that's the Myerses' place, isn't it? — over the porch roofs, using that old stepladder as a bridge. What happens when we get there, though?"

"Let's worry about it when we get there. I think we'd better get out of here just as soon as we can. It's possible that the burning will dislodge that whole pile and it'll just drift off, but if it doesn't, we'd better be out of here before it reaches us." He frowned in agitation. "We'd better get into some warmer clothes, too."

In just over ten minutes all six of them, including sixteen-month-old Teddy, were in the front bedroom. The porch roof was only an inch under water and Paul eased himself out of the window and winced as the cold water seeped into his shoes. Lindsey and his son handed out the eight-foot ladder. It would make a treacherous bridge at best, but it would have to do.

The fire was now licking strongly at the side of the frame house that had originally slammed into the Lindsey place. Even as they watched the boards turned from white to black, blistered and then burst into flame. In minutes the entire outer wall of the little house was afire and the flames roared ten or fifteen feet into the air.

Howard climbed out to help Osborne, and together the pair stretched out the ladder until it rested firmly on the slightly higher porch roof of the house next door. It spanned the distance no more than an inch above the water. Paul stepped carefully back to the window and climbed in.

"Paul," his wife's voice was calm but concerned, "how can we carry Teddy across?"

"I'll take him," Osborne said. He ripped a blanket off the bed where Lindsey had been lying and then pulled up the sheet and wrapped it twice around his chest. He held the loose ends behind him and said, "Tie these at my back, Dad, and make sure it's a good tight knot." Ted Lindsey did so and Paul said, "All right, Dottie, let me have Teddy now."

The young woman handed him the baby who, despite all the excitement, still slept peacefully. Opening the folds of cloth at his chest to form a pouch, Paul, with Dorothy's help, stuffed Teddy deeply inside and took a few steps to see how it held.

"Guess the Indians knew how to carry 'em best after

all," he said, grinning. "Come on, let's go, everyone, out on the roof. You'll get wet feet and it's slick, so make sure you hang on to one another. Howie'll help from the outside."

They assembled on the roof at the end of the ladder, ghostly figures in the reddish light of the flames. Howard announced he would go first and set off without waiting for objections. Bracing the arches of his feet against the rungs, he made his way across slowly, step by step. He grinned broadly as he stepped off on the dry porch roof next door. "Okay, Father, you're next. Be careful and take my hand as soon as you can."

The elder Lindsey started, holding Paul's hand until the distance made him release it. Three steps more and his hand locked with his son's and he was across. He stood on the roof with his feet well braced, holding Howard's hand as his son stepped a couple of rungs out on the ladder.

"C'mon, Dot, you're next."

His sister held her husband's hand as she inched out across the water. Howard clasped her free hand before she had to relinquish Paul's hold. Ethel Lindsey, still very subdued, followed safely and left only Paul on the Lindsey porch. Teddy still slumbered quietly in the impromptu sling.

He stepped carefully across as behind him the flames raced toward the house. With firm footing under him, he clasped his two hands together and smiled. "First hazard passed successfully."

Ted Lindsey was rapping sharply on the bedroom

View of Dayton looking east from Belmonte Park Hill at about noon Tuesday.
Principal body of Great Miami River to right, with Main Street bridge in
distance. Water to left (see blow-up of this below) is flooded McKinley Park.

Marooned people watch houses floating by through flooded McKinley Park
from Belmonte Park Hill. In background is Great Miami River expanse.

View from Fairgrounds Hill looking north toward downtown Dayton. Arrow indicates Union Station tower where more than four hundred were marooned for sixty hours.

Fourth and Main streets at 4:30 P.M., looking toward Ludlow Street. White, pillared building is Dayton *Daily News*.

Main Street and Monument Avenue about 8 A.M., an hour after small break in levee here but before major break in levee at head of Taylor Street.

John H. Patterson (arrow) directs rescue operations at Main and Apple streets, foot of Fairgrounds Hill, during peak of flooding.

Looking across Great Miami River into downtown area from Belmonte

To right is concrete Dayton View bridge. Water not yet crested here.

First survivors are brought to safety in NCR-built rowboats.

As waters began to recede (note high-water marks on houses), ever more rescues were made with NCR boats. (Note, also, snow on roofs.)

Refugees wait in line for relief supplies at NCR.

First flood newspaper, run off on presses at the National Cash Register Company.

FLOOD EXTRA | DAYTON DAILY NEWS | FLOOD EXTRA

Issued from the Offices of The National Cash Register Company, Dayton, Ohio

L. XXVII. No. 186.   DAYTON, OHIO, SATURDAY, MARCH 29, 1913

WORK OF RESTORING DAYTON REDUCED TO PERFECT SYSTEM

lief Has Been Extended to Every Section of Flooded District and Suffering Reduced to a Minimum. List of Dead Not Likely to Reach he Anticipated Figures---May Not Exceed 300---North Dayton nd Edgemont Situation Not As ad As Feared---Bicycle Club akes Charge of Removal of Dead nimals.

Latest information causes the general committee to again the estimates of dead. At 11 o'clock Saturday ing it was thought that the death list would not run than three hundred. At 10 o'clock W. F. Blackwell arge of the morgues, said that he did not think the er would be above 250. After that time many more were reported, and many were inquiring about per ho, they said, had been swept from roofs into the cur

is impossible to estimate the loss in dollars and cents se of the flood throughout the city. It will run into se of the flood throughout the city. It will run int llions. Fire has leveled how many costly buildings in ntral portion. Water destroyed homes and busines

The Identified Dead

Mrs. James Wallace, age 50, 105 Montgomery street. Body taken to Davis Undertaking establishment.
E. B. Clapp, age 60. Body at Central Morgue.
Christ Poock. 51 Hess street, age 65.
Virginia Snyder, age 70, 460 Howard street. Body removed to Lutherman's. 460 Howard street.
Howard Snyder, age 70. Body at Central Morgue.
Alexander Ford, age 26, 50 Ringold street. Buried Woodland Cemetery.
Mrs. Bowen, Mage 45, wife of South Main street optiman.
J. Mason, girl 4 years old. First and Foundry.
Mrs. Crummerson, or Clemson, age 90 on E. First street.
George Morganbaier, age 30. View and Warren.
John Butts age 60, found at First and Foundry.
Frankie Scott, boy, aged 5.

John McDonnell, or "Snow" McConnell, aged 40.
Miss Olive Knee, 1015 1-2 E. Fifth street.
Mr. Sortini, age unknown, killed by gas explosion, Main and Vine streets. Body found on premises.
Miss Schonk, age unknown, killed by gas explosion, Main and Vine streets. Body found on premises.
Mrs. Hazel B. Seegar, 409 Warren street, identified by Metropolitan Life insurance policy and deposit book of Germane Building and Loan association.
Mrs. Mary Young, two rings on right hand, one so left; identified by daughter.
Henry Wieseninger, 35 (formerly reported unidentified.)
Chris Pope, drowned at 1:30 o'clock Tuesday afternoon, while trying to escape on horse. Body has not been recovered. Reported by Alfred Kyer, who was marooned in Carrier building, Wayne avenue and State.

The Unidentified Dead

Male, 50, blue eyes, white, sandy hair. Found at 119 Plum street.
Male, 50, blue eyes, white, brown hair. No information.
Female child, still born.
Male, 5 years, blue eyes, white, sandy hair. Found at May and Montgomery streets.
Female, 20 years old, 5 feet 4 inches tall, blue eyes, white, sandy hair. Found on Edgar street near Second. Two and

tall, brown eyes, white, black curly hair. Found at Burns and Market street by Main Militia Friday night.
Female, 60 years old, 5 feet 1 inches, blue eyes, white, brown hair. Name unknown, body brought to Hawkins.
Male, 5 feet 2 inches, 40 years old, brown eyes, white, black hair. Found by Militia. No identification marks.
Female, 20 years old, 5 feet 7-2 inches tall, blue eyes, white, brown hair. Found

PANIC SEIZES CROWD WHEN LEVEES BREAK

Thousands of men, women and children, who through curiosity risked their lives early Tuesday morning in watching the flood at Monument avenue and Main street, fled in horror south on Main street when the water suddenly poured over the levee in the rear of the Leylor property on Monument avenue.

Only a small quantity of water came over the levee, but the a cry of terror that arose caused the crowd to become panic stricken. Fearing that a wall of water, which would drown them if they were caught, was close behind them, they rushed pell-mell down the street.

Women dragged little children and strong men trampled the weaker ones. Automobiles running at high speed through the crowd knocked many from their feet, but none were seriously injured.

A roof upper set the flooing than much as they arrived at Third and Main streets where water rushing from a break in the levee at Webster street reached them. Some were knee deep before they took refuge in office buildings along the street. As the flood reached the dry excavation for the Elder and Johnson building at Fourth and Main street it poured over the walls like a small Niagara.

Within ten minutes after the first warning cry had startled the crowd rushing down the street there was few fourth of men all of the street in the center of the business district. Even the late people did not realize that any more water than could be carried off by the storm sewers was on the streets and many lost their lives trying to reach places where they thought they would be among Franlin

COURAGE!

Appalling as the blow has been, Dayton does not despair. Never has there been so brilliant an expression of Dayton spirit, the spirit that made Dayton great. Never so great an opportunity to show the stuff of her manhood as in the days to come.

Courage sublime has been the prevailing temper of the stricken people. Dauntless and unterrified, they have accepted disaster as their inevitable lot, and turn to the morrow with fresh hope and determination.

The rallying power of Chicago, of Galveston, of San Francisco, is no less abundant in Dayton. Here a new city will be built—better, greater, more glorious than the old.

The full force of the stunning blow has not yet been felt. The people have been too full of excitement—of terrible industry to save life and to assuage suffering—to realize the calamity—to full of gratitude that they are alive. Tomorrow the test will come, but it will be met in the same spirit that the first impact of disaster was resisted.

Yesterday the catastrophe; today relief; tomorrow restoration. Dayton inconquerable, will rise incomparable, more splendid than ever. In humble submission, let us bow to the stroke of the mysterious provident that has laid us low, acknowledge the affliction, and chastened, look to the future with undimmed vision, with high resolves and unclouded optimism. Despite the horror, there can be no calamity while the old civic pride remains.

On every lip is grateful acknowledgement of the matchless generosity which has poured relief into the

N. C. R. RELIEF TRAIN GETS IN

Third Street, Looking Toward Business Section of City

A Portion of Flooded District Near N. C. R. Factory

West on First Street. Office Buildings in the Distance

Dayton Suffers From Most Destructive Flood in Its History

The Miami River valley in which Dayton is located, under ordinary conditions one of the most beautiful and peaceful valleys in this country, was suddenly transformed on Tuesday, March 25, into a channel of death and destruction. This was the culmination of a series of unusually severe wind and rain storms which had been in progress for several days throughout the north central section of the United States. As a result of these cyclones and floods a large portion of the country has been devastated from Nebraska on the west to Pennsylvania on the east.

Storm Began Easter Sunday

The storm proper did not reach Dayton until Easter Sunday, March 23, when it rained at intervals during the afternoon and night. On Monday the waters seemed to fall from the clouds in torrents, and by Monday evening, the twenty-fourth, the Miami River, which flows through Dayton, was higher than it had been at any time this year. It continued to rise rapidly and by five o'clock in the evening much of the lowlands surrounding the city and a few of the lowest streets began to fill with water. The rain continued to fall all through the night, and early Tuesday morning the blowing of steam whistles and the ringing of fire alarms and church bells gave warning to those in the lower sections to seek safety from the currents which were rapidly growing in volume and fury. Many heeded the warning and reached the higher points. Others apparently did not appreciate the gravity of the situation and hesitated to leave.

Rapid Rise of Waters

The waters after once breaking over the banks and levees rose with such alarming rapidity that only those who acted promptly were able to escape. There was no time for a second thought.

Hundreds had left their homes in the morning for their daily work only to be caught in the floods on the way and compelled to seek refuge in residences, office buildings and shops in the business districts. Thus they were imprisoned and separated from their families and with no knowledge as to the fate of those whom they had left at home a few minutes before.

The cellars were filled and the first floors of the houses in the residential districts were covered early Tuesday morning. This forced the people to the second floors, attics and roofs of their houses in order to escape with their lives. By nine o'clock in the morning the streets of the greater portion of the city were filled with floating rubbish, lumber, horses and houses. The telephones and telegraph lines were put out of service. Railroad trains could neither enter nor leave the city. There was no method of communication with the outside world or with the different sections of the city.

Terrible Plight of Refugees

The rains continued to fall during all of Tuesday and Tuesday night, and the waters as a consequence continued to rise. The air, growing cold and chilly, was filled with snow flurries. The skies were brightly illuminated at different points by fires which had broken out in both the business and residence sections of the city.

These were the conditions which faced thousands of people who were left marooned on the second floors, attics and roofs of their houses on Tuesday evening. Added to the discomforts of being without food, without heat, light and dry clothing, the worry and distress which accompanied the separation of families, and the danger of being carried away by the flood, was the apparent necessity of fighting the flames should they continue to spread. On Wednesday, the twenty-sixth, the waters began to recede and by Thursday evening or Friday morning practically all persons in the flooded district had been brought to dry land and their physical wants provided for.

Millions of Dollars Worth of Property Destroyed

This is considered one of the greatest disasters in the history of this country. It is impossible to estimate the loss and damage to property, but it will run into the hundreds of millions of dollars. In this city the merchandise on the first floors of the stores in the principal business sections of the city is completely ruined. The large plate glass windows and the expensive store fixtures are broken and destroyed.

Several business blocks have been destroyed by fire. Numerous houses have been completely wiped out of existence, while hundreds of others are so badly damaged that their repair is almost impossible. Along with the loss of the houses themselves is the furniture and personal property which is usually found in them, including many articles which cannot possibly be replaced for money alone. Horses, carriages and automobiles also numbered among the property which was swept away by the waters.

Members of Foreign Department Safe

A number of the members of the Foreign Department were in the submerged district and lost their household effects and valuable personal property. They were fortunate, however, in escaping with their lives and all were able to resume their usual duties on Monday, April 7.

The loss of life was not as great as at first estimated. Approximately one hundred bodies have so far been recovered. Others will no doubt, be found as the waters recede, but it is not likely that the number will exceed two hundred. This is remarkably low considering the nature and extent of the flood and speaks volumes for those who risked their lives in the work of rescue and for the devotion of the doctors, nurses and others who assisted in caring for the refugees.

Flood continued to be news far into April, as evidenced by this paper from April 12, eighteen days after flood began.

window of the house. "Phil!" he shouted. "Jean! You in there?" There was no answer. He motioned Howard and Paul to pull the ladder over to the other side of the porch and lay it across to the next porch roof. Then he stepped back and kicked the window out with a crash.

"Phil! Jean! Are you here?"

Still there was no answer from the Trimps. "I thought maybe they'd have gotten back from Cleveland last night," he told his family. "Good thing they didn't. Let's get moving."

The bouncing shadows from the firelight caused very treacherous footing across the ladder to the porch roof of the frame house where Charles and Wanda Myers lived with their teen-aged twin sons. The entire Myers family was in the front bedroom, and the fifteen-year-olds, Sam and Bill, climbed out to help the Lindsey family across.

Down Main Street, where crowds of people still stood on Fairgrounds Hill, they could see people gesticulating but could hear no words over the crackle of the fire behind them and the gurgle of water below. The wind had now begun to rise and was blowing directly toward them from the fire. Already the roofing of the Lindsey house was burning as bits of flaming material settled there.

Charles Myers climbed out and shook hands with the elder Lindsey, his face drawn into hard lines. "Doesn't look good, does it, Ted?"

Lindsey shrugged. He pointed to the porchless house next door to the south. "Any way we can get over to the

Thomas house, Charlie? With that wind coming this way the whole block's liable to go. We've got to try to reach the hill."

Myers, a big man in his late forties, nodded. "We might be able to make it with that ladder. Their rear bedroom window and ours are level. We were just talking to them a little while ago. Mel and Paula are both there, plus Sue and Ray, of course. It's only five feet across and we can lay the ladder from our window to theirs. But we'll have to crawl across on hands and knees."

Osborne said, "Let's get at it, then. We may not have much time."

All of them climbed into the Myerses' front bedroom, and they made quite a group. In addition to the six of the Lindsey clan there were five in the Myers family — Charles and Wanda, Sam and Bill, and Charlie's octogenarian father, Desmond Myers. When they joined the Thomases, Melton and Paula and their eleven- and thirteen-year-old children, Susan and Raymond, there would be fifteen of them.

The climb from window to window into the Thomas house was not as difficult as they'd expected. After the ladder was stretched across to the other window, a narrow mattress was placed lengthwise on it and the crawl across became a simple matter.

After they had assessed their position in the Thomas house they assembled in the front bedroom. Theodore Lindsey spoke thoughtfully.

"We may be safe here," he said, "if the wind dies a little and the fire doesn't jump from our house to the Trimps' and from there to Charlie's. We'd better hope that it doesn't, because it looks like we're stuck here. Charlie says the little house next south of here had its foundation undermined and collapsed. We can't reach it. If the fire keeps coming, we may have to take to the water. How many here can swim?"

The answer wasn't encouraging. Of the fifteen, only six — Paul and Dottie Osborne, Howard Lindsey, the Myers twins and Charlie Myers — thought they might be able to make it to the hill.

"I guess we'd better pray that a miracle of some kind douses that fire," Ted Lindsey said heavily.

At that moment, three houses to the north of them, the south wall of the now furiously burning Lindsey house fell, sending a shower of burning material through the north windows of the Trimps' house and onto their front porch roof.

✳ 7:45 P.M.
TUESDAY

The acrid pall of smoke was heavy now, and Theodore Lindsey pulled in from the front window, his face pale. He was quiet for a long time, and then he rubbed the back of his neck wearily and spoke with a grim finality.

"We have very little time. The fire can't possibly miss us now, which leaves us with only one thing to do — get out of here. We can't swim it, and it would probably be foolish to try even if all of us were excellent swimmers. Which we're not. There's nothing here we can use to make a boat or raft big enough or safe enough. I'm open to suggestions."

[185]

Paul Osborne spoke up. "That pile of drift in front," he said. "It reaches from the house here to the telephone pole. If it could hold up under our weight as we walked across it, we could get to the pole, climb to the top and then try to walk the wires over to the hill."

Lindsey nodded. "I was thinking of that. I felt if worse came to worst, we could use it as a last resort." He paused and then continued when no one else spoke. "I don't think it'll be quite as hard as it sounds at first. The lower telephone cable is thick and strong, and we can use our hands on the wires above it to steady ourselves as we walk across. No need to worry about any current in the wires. They're dead. Is there anyone who objects to trying it?"

"Do we have any other choice, Ted?" Ethel Lindsey said quietly. It was the first time she had spoken since the death of Ollie Saettel.

"Well, no, I guess not."

"Then we'd better get on with it, hadn't we?"

Howard Lindsey was first to climb out onto the debris. It was a great pile of timbers lodged against the house and leading to the roof of a garage apparently wedged or caught on something beneath the surface. Another pile of timbers and an old wagon had stacked up against the far end of the roof, held against the pole at the other end by the force of the current.

Stepping carefully, he made his way to the roof, then to the pole, where he gripped the metal spikes, ascended about halfway to the crossbars and then turned and waved. Only the small portion of floating wood between the roof and the pole had bobbed a little as he walked on it. He returned to the garage roof where the footing was stable and motioned the others to come.

The fire had by this time destroyed the Lindsey home and was now burning furiously throughout the Trimp residence. Already the eaves of the Myers house were forming channels for streams of dense smoke flowing almost like liquid, and it would not be long before it burst into flame.

One by one, the men helping the women and smaller children, they made their way to the garage roof. They moved without speaking, because nothing short of a shout could be heard above the roar of the fire. The entire roof of the Myers place had burst into flames, and the combined flames from the three residences billowed fifty feet or more into the air.

Suddenly Paul Osborne pointed upstream and shouted, dropping to his hands and knees and motioning the others to do the same. Bearing down on them was a tremendous square-cut timber fully twenty feet long. The others followed his lead and only just in time. With a bone-jarring thump the beam struck the end of the roof nearest the house. There was a grinding wrench as the garage broke loose, drifted several feet and caught again, swinging pendulously in the current.

Even though they had been kneeling, the collision of the timber with the roof tumbled Ethel Lindsey, Paula Thomas and little Raymond in a pile. The latter pair were protected by the bodies of the others, but Ethel fell toward the water. Howard snatched at his mother and pulled her back roughly, only to lose his own balance and plunge headlong into the water.

The debris on both sides of the garage had broken apart and now floated away, and Howard clung to the edge of the garage as it swung in its arc. He was quickly pulled back aboard by the twins, a sputtering, shivering, miserable figure who attempted without much success to wring some of the water out of his clothes.

Safe for the moment, the enormity of their present situation dawned over them. It was now a gap of twenty feet of vicious water between roof and pole and a slightly larger one between them and the house. The manner in which the garage swung back and forth, groaning and creaking, left serious doubts as to how long it could remain stuck to whatever was holding it beneath the surface.

Behind them the fire had leaped from the Myers house to the Thomas place before the former had even begun burning very well. There was no doubt now that they had gotten out just in time, but the untenability of their present situation was obvious to all. Susan, huddled in the crook of Paula's arm, was sobbing. The others sat or lay on the roof close together.

Theodore Lindsey stood erect on his knees and licked his lips. His face was wan, and while there was concern in his voice, it was strong and clear without hint of fear or despair.

"Although I've always gone to church regularly," he began, "I've never considered myself an especially devout man. Yet now I think I feel a closeness to God that I've never felt before. If it is His will that we should perish this night, then perish we will. I have many times heard it said that God helps those who help themselves.

We have helped ourselves, I think, to the fullest possible extent. Now we must ask the help of God, because surely only God can lead us now to safety."

He raised his eyes and continued in a softer tone, "And so we ask Your help at this time, O Lord. If it is Your will that some of us must die here, then let it be we who have lived our lives and spare those of us here who are so young and who have lived so little. We ask this in Thy name. Amen."

He looked at the group and smiled. "Howard," he said, "since you're all wet, you sit in the middle here. Paul, you have the baby in your pouch so you sit next to him and put an arm around him. Next, the smaller children up close and then the women. The men will stay on the outer edge, but everyone huddle together as closely as possible for body warmth. The less exposure we have to the cold, the more apt we are to have our strength when we need it . . . and there can certainly be no doubt that we'll need it."

It was a strange solid cluster of bodies that sat watching with fascination as the house they had left was destroyed and the fire continued southward to the ruins of the collapsed house where it seemed it might finally stop.

When there were short lulls in the blowing of the wind they could feel the radiant heat from the blaze, but mostly the wind blew hard, and the majority of the warmth was hurled away from them.

Three times in a half hour the garage on which they were perched splintered and creaked. Once one of its doors bobbed up in the water downcurrent from them and drifted away. Little by little the drifting debris was knocking off bits and pieces of the building, and Theodore Lindsey noted that the flat rooftop was considerably nearer the water than it had been when they first got out there. He knew it wouldn't be long until the others became aware of it, too. Their chances looked very slim at best.

✳ 8:20 P.M.
TUESDAY

Ray Stansbury, at nineteen, was a strapping hulk of a man. He stood four inches over six feet tall and weighed eighteen pounds over two hundred. He worked in the NCR Foundry, and the muscles of his arms and back and legs were like twisted cables. At eight-twenty this morning he had entered the water near the canal at Warren Street, and during the first six hours of the flooding had carried over 150 women and children from low flimsy buildings to other more substantial structures where they would be safer.

Gradually as the waters rose he was driven back, until by noon he was operating near the foot of the hill leading up to Miami Valley Hospital directly to the south across Apple Street. Two blocks to the west was Main Street and Fairgrounds Hill.

Twice during the afternoon he had dragged himself from the water and collapsed, gasping, on the side of the hill. Each time he was back in the water rescuing people before a quarter hour had passed.

His legs were dangerously blue from their long im-

mersion in the frigid waters, and his shirt and face
blackened with soot and grime. As darkness approached
he began slowly working his way toward Fairgrounds
Hill, where he could see the lights of lanterns and the
shadowy shapes of spectators. It took him a long time
to get there.

Twenty-two times in that short distance he fought
his way through currents that tore and pulled at him,
in order to reach people who called frantically to him
from porch roofs and upper windows of residences.
Twenty-two times he floundered back to the hillside
carrying his precious burden — a human life. Each of
these people he instructed to go immediately to NCR
for food and lodging, and then he continued his rescue
operations. Now it was exactly twelve hours since he
had begun these labors, and he was exhausted as he
had never been before. His hands were punctured and
gashed in a dozen places where they had encountered
bits of glass clinging to window frames or nails or other
sharp objects encountered beneath the muddy surface.
Three times nails had driven through the soles of his
shoes and into his feet, but it hadn't stopped him. His
back and shoulders were sore where dozens of boards
and branches and other floating matter had bumped into
him.

He moved now as in a dream, scarcely feeling the
pain or the iciness of the water. At the midpoint in the
intersection of Apple and Hill Streets, he was waist
deep in water when he lost his footing. He went entirely under the surface, and in an instant the current
had him. As if he were a rag doll, it flung him against

a telephone pole, stunning him, carried his barely resist-
ing body a block west on Apple and then a block north
on Brady to Foraker Street.

Here an eddy gripped him and spun him around and
the thought came to him, This is what it feels like to
die. I'm going to die very soon. He flung out his arms, but
the gesture was weak, uncoordinated and served only
to free him of the eddy. The current now towed him
toward Main Street.

At Main he struck another pole, and this time a flailing
hand hit a guy wire and instinctively clamped on it.
The current pulled at his body until he was virtually
lying on the surface, his face barely out of the water.
He tried to bring his other hand up to grip the wire
but could not, and again the grim thought came to him.

This is what it feels like to die.

✳ 8:30 P.M.
TUESDAY

The headlights from three trucks and half a dozen
lanterns that shone over the water on Main Street from
Fairgrounds Hill were lost in the ruddier reflection of
the fire burning two blocks north at the offset intersection
of Main and Stout Streets. It was hard to make things
out clearly in the flickering, dancing shadows. A bucket
being swept along looked like the head of a swimmer.
A broken limb jutting from a bigger branch looked like
an arm raised in mute appeal from the water as it was
pushed along.

Most of the crowd gathered near the water's edge were

intent on the fire that had floated across Main Street from Saettel's and had set the residences there afire. Few people were watching the surface of the water, but John H. Patterson was one of these.

In the dancing firelight on the water's surface he saw an object bob out of Foraker Street a block north to the edge of Main and thought for a moment that it was a log. Then it hit a telephone pole, bounced off, and an arm raised and gripped the guy wire. It was a man!

Patterson watched intently, expecting to see the individual pull himself up and wade toward the hill, knowing the water there was little more than chest high, but the movement didn't come. The hand maintained its grip but the body merely lay listlessly in the current.

Without a word, Patterson waded into the water, bracing himself to keep from being swept off his feet and clenching his teeth against the cold. As he crossed Apple, behind him he heard his name being shouted and voices pleading with him to come back, but he paid no heed. A line of fences bordered the front yards on the east side of Main Street here and he gripped the first one, step by step guiding himself along the submerged sidewalk. Twice he slipped, and his grip on the fence kept him from being pulled out into the middle of the street.

It took nearly fifteen minutes for him to reach the corner pole. Holding to the fence he reached out for the hand, but was short a foot of spanning the distance. With his free hand he stripped off his belt, fastened the strap end in the buckle and slipped the loop over the corner post of the fence. Clenching the other end of the loop tightly he moved out and this time reached the hand.

The man's face was dull, his eyes unseeing, but Patterson could hear his labored breaths. He gripped the man's wrist and tried to free him from the wire, but it was as if the big hand were welded to it.

"You! You there! Let go. It's all right, I've got you. Let go. Listen to me . . . LET GO, you're safe now!"

Dimly Ray Stansbury heard the voice. With great effort he turned his head, and for the first time became aware of Patterson's grip on his wrist. He blinked several times with returning awareness, realized the man was still shouting at him and then managed to stretch out his free hand toward him.

Instantly Patterson released the wrist holding the wire and grasped the outstretched hand. He pulled the man toward him and continued to shout to him to loose his grip on the wire, and finally Stansbury did. A moment later Patterson had the much larger man's arm over his shoulder and half walked, half dragged him back along the fence toward Apple. Nearly there he was met by two NCR rescuers who took the young man from him. The foursome safely completed their transit across Apple Street and waded out of the water.

Patterson had lost his glasses, and for a while he sat on the running board of his car beside Stansbury, regaining his own breath. In a short while he stood up and nodded to the two who had helped them ashore.

"Good work," he said hoarsely. "Now help me get

this man into the car and back to the factory. One of you will have to drive us. I'll pick up another pair of glasses at my office."

✳ 9:20 P.M.
TUESDAY

Fred Scott was a native of Montana, and he looked the part of a rugged westerner. Six feet five inches tall, he had the look of buckskin and whang leather about him, even though his lean and lithe body was clad in a suit.

Scott was twenty-five years old and an employee of the National Cash Register Company — not in Dayton, but in the Montana branch office in Helena. He had come to Dayton only a week ago to take part in the salesmen's classes being held at the home factory, to learn about the new models being produced and what advantages they would provide the consumer. It was his third such trip to Dayton, but the first time he regretted coming.

Montana had had a hard winter, and he had been looking forward to getting away from the howling winds and great drifts of snow that had choked the countryside for so long. The last thing he wanted was more of nature on the rampage, which was precisely what he was getting here in Dayton.

Because of the abrupt switch to emergency procedure at the plant this morning, classes had been canceled. More than half of the salesmen had been missing anyway, apparently marooned in their downtown hotels.

Scott was glad he had taken a tourist room only two blocks from the factory on Jasper Street.

Throughout the day he had mingled with the Main Street crowd on the north side of Fairgrounds Hill. It was an awe-inspiring sight to see the water rise higher and higher during the day until the crest had been reached around three o'clock. John H. Patterson was right there at the water's edge all day, and twice Scott had seen him wade in to the waist to lend a hand to someone being rescued.

When the explosion at Saettel's had come he had watched as horrified and as helpless as the others, sick inside to be so unable to help, not wanting to watch and yet held spellbound by the frightening drama.

The size of the crowd on the hill had fluctuated during the day, with some people leaving and others coming to stand along the water's edge as helpless and as angry at their helplessness as their predecessors had been, as Scott himself was. They were a quiet crowd, mostly — unwilling to talk to others, filled with an unreasonable shame at not being able to do anything to help.

Frequently runners would roar up to Patterson on motorcycles from the direction of NCR, talk a moment, listen while the NCR president gave instructions and then roar away again. Scott's admiration for the man had always been high, but it soared to much greater heights today. Nearly an hour ago he had watched Patterson personally take to the water in a daring rescue of an exhausted youth and he had cheered along with the rest when the executive had brought him to safety and then took him to the factory.

But the real drama of the day had been when the Saettel fire floated across Main Street and started the chain reaction fire of residences that threatened nearly a score of people. Along with the others he had watched this cluster of imperiled people move from house to house, and he had groaned along with the crowd when they became marooned in the last house with the fire advancing inexorably behind them.

Scott caught a glimpse of a flame-lighted shadowy figure crawl from the window of the last house out onto the pile of debris and then across the garage roof and the second pile of drift to the telephone pole. He watched the figure climb part way up the pole, and automatically his eyes went to the wires leading from pole to pole right to this very hill. It was their only chance, but then even this seemed stripped from them as the group became abruptly marooned on the swaying roof. Scott grinned suddenly and smacked a big fist into his palm. At last there *was* a way he could help.

He pushed his way through the crowd away from the water's edge toward the top of the hill where a large wagon, the horses gone, stood braced against a big tree. The wagon was filled with furniture and other merchandise, undoubtedly from a store. It was tied down with a crisscrossed length of manila rope, and Scott set about untying it. He was nearly finished when a large hand gripped his shoulder and spun him about.

"Looter!" A huge bear of a man spat the word at him and drew back his fist. Scott side-stepped the blow easily and drove his own fist deep into the stranger's overcoated middle. The man's breath came out in a whoosh, his hat sailed a few yards away, and he backed up a step or two before flopping in a sitting position, gasping for air.

Scott continued unwinding the rope without another glance at him, and by the time he had it coiled and looped over his head and one shoulder, the man was slowly regaining his feet. He still looked stunned.

"You'll get your rope back in a little while," Scott told the man coldly before striding off toward the crowd.

The first telephone pole on dry ground was several yards behind the outermost fringe of the crowd facing the water and he was nearly to the top before anyone even saw him climbing. When they did, they converged beneath him shouting encouragement.

The walk across the wires was almost ridiculously easy for him. Standing upright on the broad telephone cable, he was able to grip a thinner electric wire in each hand at shoulder height. Walking carefully but quickly, it took him less than ten minutes to walk the three blocks and reach the pole over the marooned group.

"Hey!" he called. "Hey there! Are you all right?"

The expressions on the faces of the group on the garage roof was first one of disbelief, immediately followed by incredible relief. Theodore Lindsey stood up and waved.

"We're all fine," he called, then added, "now that you're here. You may not know it, son, but you're an answer to prayers. Can you help us get up there?"

"Sure thing," Scott said cheerfully. "Here's a good rope. Wait'll I anchor it." He tied a noose in it and dropped it over the top of the pole, drawing it tight against the crossarm. Then he climbed down the pole spikes, uncoiling line as he descended. There was plenty of rope to spare at the bottom, and he tossed the remainder of the coil to Paul Osborne.

Wanda Myers cast a fearful look at the wires nearly twenty feet above them. "Is . . . is it hard to walk across them?" she asked.

Scott's answer was reassuring. "Not much to it if you take it slowly and watch your step. I'll help each of you up, get the wires in your hands and your feet started right. The rest'll be up to you. I don't think we should put the weight of more than one at a time on them, though, so we'd better wait until the first person reaches the next pole toward the hill before the second person starts. Who wants to go first?"

No one answered right away, and the elder Lindsey grimaced. "We don't have time for debates," he said. "This roof could go at any time. Let's get the nonswimmers off first, starting with the children. Ray, you're first. Hop to it."

The thirteen-year-old nervously grasped the rope high up as Paul lifted him. He swung toward the pole and was grabbed by Scott, but not before getting wet to his waist. Scott anchored the trailing end of the rope to one of the foot spikes and helped the boy up the pole. Soon Ray was on the way, at first edging nervously along, but then gaining confidence as he saw how easy it was. He didn't raise his feet from the cable, but pushed one forward and then drew the other up to it.

Howard was next, carrying Susan across as she clung to his back. As rapidly as possible, then, the others followed. Some made the trip rapidly, some with fearful slowness, aware of the awful water waiting just below. The only one who had any difficulty at all was old Desmond Myers. Halfway between the first two poles he slipped and his feet left the cable. His grip on the hand wires was strong, however, and he managed to regain his footing quickly.

It took the better part of an hour, but with Paul Osborne — his son still sleeping in the homemade sling — and Fred Scott bringing up the rear with the rope once again looped over his shoulder, the refugees were saved. Before these last two had gotten off the wires, the roof upon which the group had been marooned so long broke free, tipped and drifted away.

As each member of the party reached the first dry land pole on Fairgrounds Hill, the eager hands of men who had climbed up there helped them down and they were hustled to the factory one by one, where they were provided with hot food, a change of clothing and a warm dry place to sleep.

It was 10:45 P.M. when Fred Scott himself climbed down the last pole. His back ached, and he was bone weary, but for the first time since arriving here, he was glad he'd come to Dayton.

TUESDAY

✳ 9:30 P.M.

The huge young man accepted the hot soup, coffee and thick ham sandwich gratefully from an attractive girl of about nineteen in waitress garb. His face cracked in an expansive smile for her.

"Thank you, ma'am," he said. "Smells mighty good. I haven't eaten anything since breakfast. You folks sure set up fast in here." With a dip of his head he indicated the big NCR dining room in which somewhere over seven hundred refugees and rescuers and relief people were eating the same fare he had been served.

"We've served nearly three thousand today already," she told him, flashing a bright smile. "Exclusive of employees." She frowned prettily. "It's awfully bad out there, isn't it?"

He nodded soberly. "Yes, ma'am, I'm afraid it is."

"My brother Fred is out there somewhere helping to rescue people. I hope he's all right. Were you helping to rescue people?" she blushed. "I mean, your clothes look so clean and all, I just wondered if you'd gotten started yet."

The big fellow smiled. "I've done a little work out there," he said. "Got all wet, though, and my clothes were kind of muddy and torn so they gave me these. Even gave me some clean pajamas and a bunk, but I won't be usin' 'em for awhile.

"Say," he added, changing the subject, "that Patterson's quite a man, isn't he? Setting up all this relief and all."

"He seems to know what he's doing." The girl had an amused look on her face. "Did you see him out there?"

"See him! He saved my life less'n an hour ago." He told her briefly what had happened and concluded with, "Yes, sir, that Patterson's the greatest man I ever met.

Without him I wouldn't be here, and a whole lot of other people wouldn't, either. Well, if you'll excuse me, ma'am, I guess I'd better get this food eaten and get back out there and help. Maybe we'll run into each other again when this is all over. My name's Ray Stansbury. Mind if I ask you yours?"

She shook her head pertly. "No, I don't mind. It's Dorothy. Dorothy Patterson."

Stanbury looked up sharply and she laughed as she started to go back toward the serving counter. She nodded over her shoulder to him as she left.

"He's my father," she said proudly.

✳ MIDNIGHT
TUESDAY

Despite the persistent rain, the clammy chill in the air and the lack of heat, the survivors on the roofs of the buildings in the 100 block of East Third Street were very fortunate.

The smoke that had risen most of the day from the rubbled remains of the Burkhardt and Rotterman Drug Store had finally ceased, and the awful spectre of fire had disappeared with it. The stores and shops over which they walked were a treasure trove of supplies of all kinds and, other than fresh water, there was little they lacked.

Even the water situation was tolerably well taken care of by J. Harvey Kirkbride, who had, with a sort of unspoken agreement, taken over leadership of the twenty-two men, five women and two boys marooned there.

By entering the M. D. Larkin Supply Company at 113 East Third through the hatch, they secured three galvanized tubs which they placed on the roof. Each of these tubs would catch about a bucketful of water in four hours' time, which was adequate for their drinking needs.

Fresh fruits — principally apples and grapefruit — were found in the stores of the Kiefaber Company, commission merchants, at 121, and the W. L. Adamson Company, wholesale grocers, at 117, provided them with a variety of canned goods as well as tobacco.

"I think," Kirkbride addressed the group as they helped themselves to the supplies, "that each of us ought to keep a tally of what supplies he takes and uses and make every effort to repay the owners after this is all over. I rather suspect they would refuse payment, but we should nevertheless make the offer."

There was general agreement among the group at this and Kirkbride went on, "In addition, I think we'd better make a strictly-adhered-to rule right now that there will be no smoking done inside any of these buildings. If anyone cares to smoke, he'll have to go to the roof to indulge his pleasure. We all have a reasonably good idea what would happen if any one of these buildings should take fire. The chances are better than even that the whole block would burn. Does anyone object to doing his smoking on the roof only?"

There were no objections. Later in the afternoon, when the novelty of the flooded city had worn off, when less and less drifting material shot past, the group entered the hatch of the Evans Brothers Wholesale Drugs

Company at 129 — the first building west of Kirkbride's place of employment at the Johnson and Watson Company at 131 — where they obtained decks of cards and played scat and rummy and bridge to help while away the rainy hours, using boxes as tables and benches as seats.

As darkness came they moved en masse over the roof of the Patterson Tool Company, at 127, and entered the hatch of the building owned by the Cooper Saddlery, at 123. Here they found on the second floor a large supply of lap robes and horse blankets. In the swiftly dimming light they made beds on the long display tables that stretched the length of the building, each person putting down two horse blankets first and then covering himself with two or three lap robes. It was, on the whole, quite comfortable.

J. Harvey Kirkbride, however, was nervous. He felt that for some reason they were having it too good, too easy, and being supplied with too many luxuries that others were surely being denied. A premonition came to him, an omen of worse times coming and, since he was not a man given to presentiments, it bothered him considerably.

He suggested that they form a two-man lookout throughout the night to keep alert for possible unexpected dangers. They all thought it was a good idea and, since there were so many of them there, decided on hourly shifts among the men so that none of them would be deprived of very much sleep. One of the tasks of the lookouts was to check the depth of the water, which they did by descending the stairs of the Johnson and Watson building until the water level was reached. Here Kirkbride knew almost exactly how far above floor level the stairs were, and with a crayon found in the Evans Brothers Company they marked the water level along the steps.

At midnight the highest stage here was marked. It was nine feet eight inches above floor level, indicating somewhat over twelve feet of water on Third Street — and this area of East Third Street was one of the highest areas in the entire downtown sector.

Meanwhile, at the Main Street bridge, the river gauge continued to hold steady at twenty-nine feet.

Wednesday: 12:30 A.M.

DAYTON had never before seen a night as dark as this one. With electricity gone and hardly more than a handful of usable kerosene lamps scattered about the city, there was an eerie, frightening quality about this night.

There was, first and foremost, the constant gurgle of waters, somehow sounding all the more treacherous when sliding by in the darkness. Occasionally would come the sounds of a shout, a scream, a splash. Now and then shots were fired, but mostly it was quiet except for the water.

Yet, on the south edge of town was a bright oasis — a huge building blazing with light, throbbing with the hum of machinery and milling with the activities of upwards of five thousand people. Horns honked here occasionally, there was the clatter of dishes and silverware as people ate, the murmur of hundreds of voices.

The upper windows on the north side of the building

were crowded with people looking over the darkened city, seeing nothing and yet knowing the horror that was there, the misery and the tragedy. Some of these people cried chokingly, having seen loved ones perish in the water or otherwise separated from them with no idea of their fate.

At his desk on the ninth floor, awake after a two-hour nap, John H. Patterson jotted down thoughts that struck him concerning what more could be done to help those still marooned without food, water or heat — many without even shelter.

And while life for many was ending in the cold black waters downtown, new lives were coming into existence. Two babies, both boys, were born in the fourth floor emergency maternity ward. They were the first of many to be born here, and though neither of them had been given names as yet, both were to have names they could wear with pride, for the first one would be called John H. and the second was named Cash. They weren't the only ones to be so named.

In one day the NCR had become a city unto itself: in the basement clothing salvaged from the flood was being disinfected, cleaned and dried. Three women from the Services Department tacked up hastily lettered signs throughout the building, telling people where to go to get food and clothing, medical service, comfortable beds, freshly brewed coffee and even emergency dental service.

A few reporters from the closer cities — Columbus, Cincinnati, Xenia, Lebanon, Springfield — began to show up and were provided with desks, typewriters and cots on the second floor. Only the cots were thus far unused.

Telephones and telegraph were still useless, but the latter was expected to be operative within another twelve hours and the telephones not long after that.

For the third time that night, John H. Patterson went to the roof. Despite the chill of the air and the dampness, half a hundred refugees were still up there looking to the north. They could see nothing, but their eyes nevertheless strained to see and their thoughts and prayers were almost a physical force in the air.

Patterson walked to the edge apart from the others and glanced at the buzz of activity below. Another truckload of half a dozen boats chugged eastward on Stewart Street. A constant procession of people entered and left the big building. To the refugees the plant was a haven of light and hope in a world gone mad.

"This can not — *must* not! — happen again," Patterson said softly before he reentered the building.

✳ 1 A.M.
WEDNESDAY

"All right out there, young feller?"

In the palpable darkness of the library building it was difficult even to see the shadowy shape of someone standing close at hand, and it was impossible for the man at the window to see the youth in the tree. It was also hard to hear over the continuing murmur of the water and the man called out again.

"Hey there! You in the tree. You still all right?"

The voice came faintly, weary and discouraged.

"I'm here. Still here."

"Is the water going down any?"

"I can't tell," the youth shouted. "I don't think it is. I don't think it ever will. I'm so cold!"

"Hang on, boy. Hang on. It'll be morning before you know it and somehow we'll help you. Hang on!"

"I don't imagine I'll be going anywhere," the voice replied bitterly.

McKenny turned from the window and groped his way back to where he'd been sitting on the floor. He stepped on his bowler hat and crushed it and cursed softly. A short distance away he could just barely make out the recumbent figures of Mary Althoff and the young woman, Laurie Tomlinson, snuggled together beneath the warm buffalo hide. Beside them in a sitting position dozed the janitor.

The librarian had at first objected strongly against the use of the furs in the museum's collection, but gradually weakened as the arguments for their use became stronger. Even Harvey had agreed with them, and it was he who finally coaxed her into acquiescence.

"Ain't like as if we was gonna' burn 'em or destroy 'em, Miss Althoff," he said. "Won't harm 'em at all just to use 'em to keep the chill off. Likely all of us'll get pneumonia if we don't."

She had agreed at last, and down from the walls came the zebra and buffalo skins, the leopard and tiger hides. Each of the party had one for a cover except the two women who shared the large buffalo hide, and the guilt she felt at first over using them disappeared as the warmth beneath the cover grew and for the first time since early morning she was able to stop shivering.

[209]

Outside the rain and sleet pelted down steadily and in the back of each of their minds was a continuing deep pity for the man in the tree outside. There had been fear that he would fall asleep and tumble from his limb despite the reins with which he had tied himself to the trunk. As darkness fell, shortly after the oil tank had boomed past, the men had decided to alternate in going to the window throughout the night to call the youth, to say anything, just to keep his spirits up and his hopes alive, to keep him from going to sleep and falling and, most of all, to reassure him that someone cared what happened to him.

It was a long uncomfortable night for all of them, but each felt almost regally comfortable when he compared his own lot to that of the man in the tree. And the same thought was in the mind of each of them.

Would he still be there in the morning?

✱ 6 A.M.
WEDNESDAY

A hoarse shout from the steps leading down to the main floor of the Public Library brought the entire upstairs group on the run. They crowded down to the landing and looked at the janitor, who was crouched on the steps a little way below them.

"Mr. Harvey, what is it? Are you hurt?" Mary Althoff's eyes were frightened.

Harvey turned and grinned at them. "No, ma'am," he said. "Sorry if I scared you. Didn't mean to. Just wanted to give you some good news. After I called to the boy out there in the tree about three o'clock this mornin', I crept down these steps kinda easy like, an' when I got to the water I scratched a mark at the water line with my penknife." He pointed excitedly, like a little boy. "Look here. Water's gone down two whole steps since then. It's recedin', by gum. Might be it'll be mostly gone by this evenin'."

"Thank heavens," Mary sighed. "It seemed like it was never going to stop rising. Now if it would only stop raining."

"Amen to that," Laurie agreed. "I've seen enough water to last me the rest of my life."

" 'Cept for drinking," said one of the older men, Silas Houghton. "My throat feels awful. I'd give anything for a big glass of water." The overhang of the eaves had made it impossible for them to catch any rain water.

"And a nice big breakfast," added Hugh Warder.

"I'll say," Billy Denton agreed. "Like hotcakes and sausages and eggs and —"

"That's enough!" Mary said sharply. "We don't have those things, and we won't feel any better thinking about them. What we need to do is to try to think of some way to help that poor young man in the tree out there."

Robert McKenny concurred. "He's got a lot of courage to hang on like that all night in this weather. I expect he's half frozen. I just wish there *was* some way we could help him. Maybe some boats'll be out in the streets this morning and someone'll be able to rescue him. I guess the best thing we can do is to keep calling to him to keep his spirits up." He walked back upstairs and went to the window and the others followed him.

The pity that had filled Mary Althoff for the youth clinging so tenaciously in the tree was almost overpowering, as was the frustration of wanting to help him so badly and yet being able to do nothing. More than any of the others she had called to him, offering encouragement and hope. At last her voice had given out and she could barely whisper. She longed desperately for a drink and then wondered if she could even swallow it if she had it. Her throat felt as if it were nearly swollen shut. She waved to the youth and left the window, but her cheerful smile faded immediately, and she was sure it would be the last time she'd ever seen him. She knew if it had been her out there she couldn't have held on anywhere near that long under such conditions, especially since he had been in the water. She didn't see how he could possibly last much longer.

She slumped to the floor with her back to one of the museum cases, drawing her knees up against her chest and locking her arms around her legs. She dropped her forehead to her knees and closed her eyes and quietly asked God to spare the young man's life.

✳ 8:50 A.M.
WEDNESDAY

Through the night the beams of ceilings and floors of Steele High School had screeched and groaned at the pressure of the waters, and by dawn's early — and gloomy — light, the imprisoned teachers became deeply concerned at the size of the cracks that had developed — cracks from which every now and then a small shower of plaster would fall as they fluctuated with the pressure of the waters.

Shortly before 9 A.M. the tower trembled so badly that the teachers were knocked from their feet. This was accompanied by an increased groaning from the strained walls and ceilings.

"This is a very old building," William Schantz said soberly, "and I wouldn't be at all surprised if it collapsed. I think we might be wise to try to escape, perhaps to the roof of the dry cleaners adjoining us to the south."

The others agreed and followed him out of the tower into the second floor hallway. No sooner had they closed the door behind them than a terrifying roar thundered through the building, accompanied by vibrations so strong that the whole party was forced to brace themselves against the walls and each other to keep from being thrown to the floor. As quickly as it had begun, the noise stopped, and the educators looked at one another in wonderment.

Frank Anderson wheeled and jerked open the door to the tower room they had just vacated and was greeted by daylight and an unobstructed view of the outside.

The tower was gone — lost in the swirling waters below.

Paradoxically, directly across Monument Avenue from the great stone hulk of the high school stood the ancient log cabin called Necom Tavern. It was directly in the path of the waters pouring through the levee, yet stood firmly, wet and muddied, but otherwise undamaged.

✱ 8:55 A.M.
WEDNESDAY

John Barringer showed the mud-bespattered man into the president's office and said, "Mr. Patterson, this is Mr. George F. Burba, secretary to Governor Cox."

Patterson gripped the visitor's hand strongly, but his smile was mechanical. "Mr. Burba," he said, "I'm glad you were able to get here. You look as if you may have had a difficult time. Please sit down."

Burba sank gratefully into a big leather chair and released a long wheezing breath. "Very difficult," he agreed. "The governor ordered me to come here immediately after hearing about the situation. Unfortunately he gave me no magic formula for getting here. It has taken me over sixteen hours."

"Conditions are bad between here and Columbus?"

"Bad, yes, but not as severe as here. Many roads and bridges are washed out, as I found through personal experience." He chuckled drily. "Had to backtrack all the way to Chillicothe before finally getting through."

"I suspect you're tired and hungry, then. Would you care to refresh yourself and perhaps take a nap before we go out to inspect what we can of the city?"

Burba shook his head. "I think we better get at that first. The governor is waiting."

"As are the thousands marooned in the city here," Patterson said bluntly. "Very well, let's get started."

✳ 10:15 A.M.
WEDNESDAY

The water lapped hungrily a short distance below the windows of the staid two-story brick residence at the southwest corner of Third and Wilkinson Street, home of eighty-seven-year-old Dr. John Charles Reeve and his invalid wife, Emma.

The house was on the western edge of the downtown business district, and Dr. Reeve had chosen it with one principal belief in mind: that it stood on ground high enough to be safe from the flood waters that periodically inundated the city. The worst of these had been the flood of '66, when the old physician had been a vigorous forty years old and was looking for a better site for his home and office in the rapidly growing city.

Now, sitting at a small desk by the front window upstairs, his wife asleep on her bed nearby, Dr. Reeve reflected on his choice of location over twoscore years ago. The flood of '66 had been terrible, and yet, this plot of ground right here had stood high and dry, safe on a little knoll. He had kept the thought in mind for several years, and then early in 1870 when it was put up for sale he bought it and built this house.

The old doctor shook his head sadly, and for the first time felt a stir of thankfulness for his wife's blindness. At least she was spared seeing this devastation.

He reached into the drawer and took out fresh stationary and began a letter to his eldest son, Sidney, who lived in Thompkinsville, New York. Perhaps the letter would never be delivered or perhaps his son might get it after the writer was long since dead, but at least it would give him something to do for awhile, and somehow in the writing of it he felt better and his far distant son seemed closer.

He smiled abruptly at a paradoxical thought. His daughter Mary lived with her husband, Robert Dexter, just across the Great Miami River in Dayton View, hardly a mile away. Yet, at this moment, she was no more easily within reach than was Sidney. He was glad they lived on high ground over there, far above the level of the water, and wished there was some way of letting her know that he and her mother were safe. Not comfortable, perhaps, but safe nonetheless. His younger son, Charlie, who fortunately had gone out of town several days ago, would be worried too, but there was no help for it. The old doctor clucked his tongue and began to write:

Wednesday, March 26, 1913
10:15 a.m.

Dear Son:

I am sitting at upper window. Mother's room. Outside a raging torrent pours down Wilkinson Street, a mighty river down Third Street toward west. No human being in sight. No sign of life. Silent as the grave. Below, piles on piles of wreckage. A fine piano lying in our yard. Fortunately, yesterday at 7 a.m. I had gotten breakfast at the Arcade; oatmeal and coffee. Brought same to Mother. The danger whistles had sounded before I was

up. I suppose for break of levee. I did not much care,
did not think of possibilities. I banked on great flood of
'66 when this lot, house not then built, stood high and
dry, while all around was overflowed. Not even when
water came into yard. Now it came so fast I had to
hustle to get Mother to the stairs. Now, since last evening it has fallen nearly four feet, and as we passed last
night in total darkness with only one piece of candle two
or three inches long, I made an effort to get my lamp
from back office. I stripped to the buff, got down to the
last step, dared not take the next. So cold. Room so full
of floating furniture that I could not have made my way
through it to the lamp. I was in to my armpits.

We have a good supply of crackers. A few nuts. A few
apples. This morning young men from roof on house next
west gave us eggs and shredded wheat. We have no
water. No light. No salt for egg, no telephone connection.
No cars, no papers, nothing. Yes, we have natural gas
and know how to appreciate it. Neither one next door
has it. I boiled an egg soft, for Mother. First thing she
has kept down. Have some hard-boiled for my dinner.

Mary, we know, is worrying fearfully. We can get no
word to her or from her. The front and side of our house
is a raging torrent, a sea up to Callahan Buildings. Two
streetcars stand in front of old Winters home. The water
just over the tops of their windows. Inside house, went
over mantles. You know the rest. All night in the darkness, crashing and creaking of furnace pipes in cellar,
the banging of furniture floating about below. I could
not sleep. Do you wonder?

The muffled sound of hoarse labored breathing came to him over the gurgle of the waters, and he paused to look out the window. A large dray horse was being buffeted along by the current. At the corner it was caught briefly by an eddy and sucked down out of sight, only to reappear a moment later a dozen feet away, its mouth open wide to suck in great gasps of air. Within a minute it had disappeared to the west on Third Street toward the main river current. The doctor bit his lower lip and returned to the letter.

Pitiful to see the horses swimming for their lives. No foothold for them since yesterday, and now one has just struggled along and been swept down Third Street.

A soft moan from the bed caused him to turn. He lay down his pen and walked over to the bed, then sat on the edge of it and leaned over to press his lips to those of his wife. She smiled and put her hand to his face, running her fingers gently down his cheek. Her voice was a croak that grated past cracked lips.

"The most handsome doctor in Dayton needs a shave," she murmured. "And his wife would very much like a drink of water."

The old doctor frowned, then kissed her again. There was no water, but he took a glass with some cold coffee in it from the bedside table and held it to her lips. She swallowed twice and wrinkled her nose but said nothing. In a few minutes she had fallen asleep again, and he replaced the glass and stood up. There was about one cup of coffee left in the pot. He licked his lips at the thought of a steaming hot cup of coffee but did not take any. Emma would need all the liquids they had — and what they had would not last very long.

"Oh, God," he prayed softly, "let this end, let this end."

It began to rain very lightly and he wished he had a receptacle to put on the window ledge to possibly catch some of the precipitation. Then he thought of the old teakettle sitting on the little stove in the huge bathroom down the hall and he went out of the room to get it.

✳ 10:20 A.M.
WEDNESDAY

The first telegraph lines were open at NCR when John H. Patterson and George Burba returned from their initial inspection tour. Burba sent his first report to Governor Cox immediately.

JAMES M COX GOVERNOR STATE CAPITOL COLUMBUS SITUATION IN DAYTON VERY BAD STOP LITTLE EXAGGERATION FROM PRELIMINARY REPORTS STOP FAMINE AND SICKNESS LIKELY TO ENSUE IF EXTENSIVE RELIEF DOES NOT COME PROMPTLY STOP SUFFERING WIDESPREAD AND SEVERE STOP ENTIRE DOWNTOWN AREA UNDER TWELVE TO TWENTY FEET OF WATER STOP J H PATTERSON HAS CONVERTED NATIONAL CASH REGISTER CO INTO MASSIVE AND REMARKABLY EFFECTIVE RELIEF STATION BUT MUCH MORE HELP NEEDED STOP FOOD MEDICAL SUPPLIES CLOTHING BADLY NEEDED STOP EIGHT SQUARE MILES OR ONE HALF CITY INUNDATED STOP WATER CRESTED MIDAFTERNOON YESTERDAY AND DROPPED ELEVEN

INCHES SINCE THEN STOP NO ACCURATE ESTIMATE OF DEATHS BUT TOLL MAY RANGE FROM MINIMUM OF ONE THOUSAND UP STOP MARTIAL LAW WILL BE NEEDED WHEN WATERS RECEDE STOP MORE TO FOLLOW

BURBA

The executive secretary turned to Patterson. "That," he said, "will help to get things moving. And now, I believe I wouldn't mind at all having a good hot cup of coffee before we resume our inspection."

✴ 10:55 A.M.
WEDNESDAY

Richard Hultgren, chief of the NCR motorcycle emergency squad of fifty riders, finally located the company president and the governor's secretary at the high-water mark on Fifth Street near Dutoit in East Dayton. They were sitting in Patterson's car watching with interest the launching of six more NCR boats.

A fair-sized crowd was gathered here, watching the rescue work and cheering loudly whenever a survivor was brought ashore, which was frequently. These were being taken to Huffman School at Huffman and Fifth Streets for emergency care. Burba expressed admiration openly for the way the rescue work was being carried out.

Upon pulling to a stop beside the car, Hultgren tapped the bill of his cap and handed two telegrams to his chief. Patterson looked at them, handed one to George Burba and opened the other.

JOHN H PATTERSON NCR CO DAYTON O

MY SINCERE SYMPATHY TO YOU AND YOUR FELLOW
DAYTONIANS IN THE DISASTER YOU ARE UNDERGOING
STOP REST ASSURED ALL EFFORTS ARE BEING MADE TO
PROVIDE IMMEDIATE RELIEF AND AID STOP RED CROSS
ON WAY TO SCENE AND HAS COLLECTED THOUSANDS
OF DOLLARS FOR RELIEF STOP HAVE SPOKEN TWICE TO
PRESIDENT WILSON WHO IS GRAVELY CONCERNED STOP
HE IS SENDING SECY OF WAR GARRISON AND STAFF FROM
SURGEON GENERALS OFFICE AND NATIONAL PUBLIC
HEALTH SERVICE TO ARRIVE IN DAYTON SATURDAY IF
POSSIBLE STOP WAR DEPARTMENT HAS ALREADY SHIPPED
RATIONS FOR HALF MILLION PEOPLE WHICH SHOULD
REACH YOU LATE TOMORROW OR FRIDAY STOP I AM
MUCH IMPRESSED WITH YOUR HANDLING OF SITUATION
STOP HEREBY APPOINT YOU PRESIDENT OF DAYTON
CITIZENS RELIEF ORGANIZATION WITH FULL AUTHORITY
TO ACT FOR AND IN BEHALF OF DAYTON AND TO TAKE
CHARGE FOR THE PRESENT AND FUTURE UPBUILDING OF
CITY STOP OFFICIAL ORDER TO FOLLOW STOP REQUEST
HOURLY REPORTS OF SITUATION THERE

                              JAMES M COX GOVERNOR

Patterson smiled thinly, the irony of his "appointment"
not lost on him. He handed the telegram to George
Burba who, after a moment's hesitation, handed his own
to Patterson. It read:

GEORGE F. BURBA CARE OF J H PATTERSON NCR CO
DAYTON O

TELEGRAM RECEIVED AND ACTED UPON STOP HAVE SET

GEARS IN MOTION ON MANY FRONTS AND AID YOU REQUESTED IS COMING STOP APPOINTED PATTERSON PRES OF CITIZENS RELIEF ORGANIZATION AND DIRECT YOU WORK CLOSELY WITH HIM AND KEEP ON TOP OF SITUATION STOP STILL IN CONTACT WITH OPERATOR AT DOWNTOWN DAYTON TELEPHONE OFFICE STOP HIS EVAL-UATION OF SITUATION IN CENTER OF CITY EVEN WORSE STOP GEN GEO WOOD ADJ GEN ONG IS IN DAYTON AND WILL TAKE COMMAND IF AND WHEN HE CAN BE REACHED STOP MEANWHILE COL ZIMMERMAN OF FIFTH INF DIS-PATCHED WITH HUNDRED MEN TO ASSUME MARTIAL COMMAND STOP TELEPHONE OFFICIALS PROMISE LINES OPEN TO NCR BY THE AFTERNOON STOP CONTINUE TO TRANSMIT REGULAR EVALUATIONS OF ENTIRE FLOOD SITUATION

COX

✳ 11:05 A.M.
WEDNESDAY

Billy Denton was first to see the boat, even before the youth in the tree saw it, and he waved and yelled excitedly. "A boat! A boat! They're coming for him. He'll be saved. Hey, out there! You in the tree. Here comes a boat for you!"

The group in the library crowded to the windows. A boat made of new, unpainted lumber with two men in it made its way laboriously upstream from the west on Second Street and turned south on St. Clair. The current was not quite so strong now as it had been yesterday and during the night, though it was by no means weak and it was still hard work to breast the current, and they rested frequently, allowing the boat to bump along gently against the sides of buildings on the west side of St. Clair, where they hung on grimly.

Hugh Warder stuck his head out and yelled toward the boat and when he saw that they had heard him pointed at the young man in the tree. One of them waved, and they nosed the boat toward the youth and rowed.

They were going mainly with the current now and it was easier, but they misjudged slightly and didn't backwater in time. The bow of the boat struck the tree with a bad jar, but it didn't upset, and the man in front grasped the youth's extended hand. The oarsman held onto the tree while the other man helped the youth untie himself and get into the boat. Then they started toward the library.

It was easier rowing when they swung into the backwater formed by the building. When they got close enough, the man in the bow tossed a rope attached to the boat to Warder, who caught it defly and pulled them close. The water level was a full eight feet below their window, but when McKenny and Harvey leaned out they could grasp the hands of the boatmen when they stood.

"By golly, you're a sight to see!" McKenny said gleefully. "There's ten of us up here, so you'll have to make more than one trip. Guess you'd better take the women first and then —"

"Sorry, mister," interrupted the man who had been rowing. "We're not taking anyone. We're dropping him off." He shoved a thumb at the young man who crouched low in the boat between them, his body wracked with uncontrolled trembling.

"Dropping him off?" McKenny's tone was incredulous. "But he's been up in that tree since yesterday morning. Twenty-six hours! He needs food and water and heat. We don't have anything like that here. You've got to help us!"

"Mister," put in the man in the bow tiredly, "we'd like nothing better than to take you all to a better place, but we've got our orders."

"Orders? *Orders?* What orders?" he demanded. "From whom?"

"From John H. Patterson, that's who from. We're from NCR and we got one of the first boats they're turning out in the carpentry shop there. Mr. Patterson's sending out all the help he can, but he told us the first and most important thing we had to do was to get anybody who was hanging in a tree or pole to safety. The nearest place that's safe, that is, and then go look for others."

His companion nodded. "You're all right here," he said. "Maybe you don't have food and water right now, but there's lots of others who're worse off. Soon as they're taken care of we'll be back for you. We gotta keep moving. Grab hold of this boy's hands and pull him in there when I lift him up."

Reluctantly and with bitter disappointment, they did so. As soon as they had him safely inside on the floor the man in the bow said, "Okay, turn loose the rope," which Warder did. The boatman coiled it as they drifted away and then he looked up and shouted sympathetically,

"We'll be back again, don't worry. You'll be all right until then." With a minimum of maneuvering they disappeared south on St. Clair Street.

Inside the library the youth lay face down, clinging to the dry wood floor as if it would suddenly vanish and he would again find himself in the tree. His clothes were soggy and his skin a clammy bluish color. He was breathing rapidly and was still shivering terribly. He was about eighteen years old and quite good looking.

Swiftly Warder stripped off the boy's jacket and shirt, removed his own heavy mackinaw shirt and put it on him. He tossed the soggy clothing aside and Mary Althoff picked them up and hung them on the antlers of a mounted moose head. Shoes and socks came off next, and Warder rolled him over on his back.

"Someone hand me that buffalo skin," he ordered Laurie ran across the room and brought it back. Warder spread it over the youth with the fur side next to him and tucked it snugly around his body, leaving exposed his arms, legs and head. "All right," he said without looking up "three more people to help massage him. One on each arm and leg."

With his pocketknife he made a cut in each of the youth's trouser legs just above the knees. He ripped the damp cloth all the way around and pulled the severed sections off his legs. The others in the group watched him as if he were performing major surgery.

"C'mon," he said savagely, "don't just stand there! Someone on the other leg and two on the arms. Massage!"

He bent to the task on the youth's right leg, briskly

rubbing and kneading the flesh of calf and foot, slapping it stingingly occasionally. He didn't even look up as Mary Althoff and Laurie Tomlinson went to work on the arms and Robert McKenny took the other leg.

Slowly a more normal coloring began coming back and the shivering decreased, but they continued working. After twenty minutes the four were relieved by four others, and the massage continued for another ten minutes. The shivering had stopped now except for an occasional shudder that ran through the youth's body. His cheeks were flushed and all four extremities were very red and warm.

Mary brought over three more skins and tucked them around him, covering his arms and wrapping the feet as in swaddling. When she finished she looked at the youth's face and he was asleep. She bowed her head and wept.

✳ 1:10 P.M.
WEDNESDAY

Wilcox Hartley, who had spent twenty-six long cold hours in a tree in Cooper Park, awoke inside the library's museum considerably refreshed. He told the group who crowded around him that he lived a dozen blocks away on Dutoit Street near East Second. He had been coming toward downtown on his horse when the levee broke at the head of Taylor Street and both he and his horse had been swept along for three or four blocks before managing to reach footing on a loading platform beside a factory. It was a precarious position, and before a quarter hour had passed the platform supports were undermined and it had collapsed, plunging horse and rider back into the savage current. That was when they had been swept into Cooper Park to that tree where the horse had drowned and his rider had lived.

Although he'd had only two hours of sleep, the change in Hartley was remarkable. With the vigor of the very young he had swiftly thrown off the exhaustion of his ordeal and now sat up with his back to the wall, still covered with the warm skins. They listened to his story eagerly, delighted with his bright personality and easy way of speaking.

"So that's the sad sad story of little Willie Hartley," he said, flashing his even teeth in a broad grin. "I'm glad to say the ending is considerably better than the one I wrote while perched out in that darned tree."

He pulled the skins down a bit and looked at his chest. "Whose shirt is this?" he asked.

"Mine," Warder answered, "but keep it on. Yours is probably still damp. This long underwear of mine is plenty enough for me."

"No," Hartley said, standing up, "you take it. I'm fine."

Despite their protestations he removed the shirt and handed it to Warder. "Where's mine now?" he asked.

Mary walked over to the moose head and felt the shirt. She wrinkled her nose. "It's still damp and cold," she said.

"That's all right," Hartley replied. "It won't dry in this clammy air near as well as it will if I put it back on."

Mary shrugged and handed the shirt to him. The youth made a weird expression as the coldness of it hit his skin and set the group to laughing. It was the first time any of them had laughed since this all began, and it did wonders for their morale. He buttoned front and sleeves and then turned and bowed gaily to Mary and Laurie who were standing side by side.

"If you ladies will forgive an unkempt appearance," he said, "I'll leave my shirttail out for the time being." He laughed brightly at their smiles and did a little jig step in his bare feet. With disheveled hair, the legs of his trousers ripped off above the knees, shirttail out and no socks or shoes on, he might well have been a young version of Robinsin Crusoe. It was as the group laughed aloud at his antics that the second explosion came.

A heavy, ear-pounding concussion, it broke more of the museum windows and jarred them all. They assembled at a previously smashed window and saw that another section of the Burkhardt and Rotterman Drug Store had blown up, collapsing much of the rear quarters that had survived the earlier blast and raising a billowing cloud of white mortar dust. As this dust settled and they could see the ruins better, Harvey suddenly pointed.

"Oh-oh," he whispered, "a fire!"

A flame no bigger than that of a lantern turned up high showed brightly in a shadowed hollow of the debris. Gradually the flickering weakened and it seemed that it would go out and then unexpectedly it spread out considerably in a deep blue flame.

"Alcohol," McKenny said. "They must've had a whole barrel of it in there."

The flame spread further, changing now to a bright

reddish yellow and throwing up dense smoke. A small cluster of men on the roof of the building to the west — the Finke Brothers Notions Store — tossed a rope down to some men who had scrambled out of the wreckage away from the fire. They wasted no time climbing the rope to the roof some twenty feet above them.

Hypnotized by the flames as if they had been moths, the eleven refugees in the window of the library watched the fire grow ever larger, and now even the crackling of the blaze could be heard. Soon the entire pile of rubble was blazing furiously and great chunks of burning matter raised by the heat of the fire shot upward and clung in the eaves of a wooden building next door which housed a small restaurant. Even as they watched, the entire wall of this building started burning.

People poured out of windows at the rear of the Hoover Livery Barn at 25 North St. Clair and attempted to reach the tobacco warehouse across the alley to the north. A few managed to swim across the awful current, but at least two disappeared under the surface as they watched.

Now the flames leaped into the stable to the north and to the eaves of the Finke Brothers store to the west, and suddenly a stream of people was hurrying away from rooftop to rooftop.

"Oh, God," Harvey muttered, "the whole block's going to go."

In that block — bounded on the south by Third Street, to the west by Jefferson, to the north by Second Street and to the east by St. Clair — more than three hundred people were trapped.

✳ 1:15 P.M.
WEDNESDAY

Most of J. Harvey Kirkbride's party were on the top floor of the Evans Brothers store when the blast rocked the buildings. They pounded up the steps and through the hatchway onto the roof and saw that the remains of the Burkhardt and Rotterman store was gone. Kirkbride and a few of the men crossed the roof of the Johnson and Watson place and climbed down the rope to the lower roof of Finke Brothers to look at the rubble.

At the rear of the smoking pile, pinned by water and blossoming fire toward the front, seven men had crawled from the ruins. They stood with their backs to the wall with the horror of their predicament etched on their faces. Every passing moment the flames grew larger, whipped by the stiff wind blowing across Cooper Park.

Kirkbride raced back to the rope, calling to those still above as he ran. "Untie that rope up there and toss it down. Hurry! There are men trapped down below."

In short order he had the rope tied to the chimney of the Finke Brothers store and lowered the end to the men standing along the wall. Remarkably, none was hurt, and they scurried up the rope with no wasted time. When they were safely on top, Kirkbride untied the rope and tried to toss it back up to the men still atop the Johnson and Watson building, but the rope fell short and a spear of panic touched him. Already the east cornice of the notion store was beginning to burn.

Kirkbride looked about swiftly and then ran to pick

up a U-shaped section of lead pipe tossed to the roof by the blast. He tied the end of the rope to it and motioned the others out of the way. Then he started the weighted line swinging around his head, gradually letting out more rope until it was whirring about in a seven-foot circle. With a great heave he shot it upward and it sailed neatly over the edge of the roof above. It didn't take them long to rejoin the higher group.

"All of you," Kirkbride said, as they clustered around him, "head across these roofs to the last one on this level — that's Sol Rauh's wholesale liquor place. On your way, pick up a few items of food from the Adamson Company and put it in your pockets. Don't get so much you weigh yourself down, but enough to feed you once or twice, anyway. Jess and I will get the rope and bring up the rear, closing the hatches behind us to help keep the fire from jumping."

It was a good idea, but by the time the group reassembled he saw that the efforts had been in vain. Though the buildings were equipped with fire walls and the hatch doors were metal lined, the fire was simply too hot and already had eaten through Finke Brothers into Johnson and Watson and was now sending up boiling billows of dense black smoke from the Patterson Tool Company. Even as they watched, a portion of Kirkbride's building roof collapsed and a fearsome ball of flame shot skyward. Though it was still seven buildings away from them, the heat of the fire reached them and the roar and crackle, punctuated by frequent small explosions of combustibles, made it almost impossible to speak and be heard.

With the hammer he had taken from the Patterson Tool firm, Kirkbride broke open the hatch of the liquor company, and the entire group of thirty-six people followed him down the stairs to the second floor. Here they climbed out of a rear window onto the roof of a low shed where the water reached just to the eaves. They skirted the Shauer Distilling Company at 105 East Third and broke into a second floor window of the Beckle Building which housed the Fourth National Bank, on the northeast corner of Third and Jefferson.

It was quite cold, and few of the refugees had warm coats with them, so most had taken along at least one lap robe or horse blanket from the Cooper Company in addition to tins of food and a little water.

Behind them the fire advanced very rapidly, jumping from building to building and seemingly little hampered by the protective fire walls.

This perplexed Kirkbride until, as they paused to regain their breath, he saw how it was happening. The fire was not going through the fire walls, but actually skirting them, creeping rapidly along the wooden cornices, curling around the walls and breaking windows with the heat, then being sucked inside the building to kindle new fuel.

From the front windows of the Beckle Building they could see the Beckle House Hotel directly across Jefferson Street, nearly every window filled with people — more than two hundred of them in view. With the thundering current rushing down Jefferson as it was, however, they quickly discarded any hope of attempting to cross over here.

They trooped up to the third floor and from a north window here they climbed to the adjoining roof of the Traction Depot. They tried to raise the heavy metal hatch cover, but found it was securely locked from the inside — a fact already discovered to their dismay by the seventy-seven people trapped inside the building, who were now clustered in a fearful group on the second floor, but whose presence was not known to Kirkbride's party.

The roofs to the north of the Traction Depot were sharply angled, making walking on them impossible, and so now they found their escape route limited to the narrow cornice ledges high above the roily waters. In a cautious single file they followed these along the Jones and McDermont buildings to the Simms Building on the southeast corner of the alley. They broke a window to gain entry to the building and went down to the second floor, searching for some way to cross the alley to the Groneweg Bindery. There was none. They had come, it seemed, as far as they could.

Behind them, its flames shooting a hundred feet or more into the air, the fire began eating at the walls of the Beckle Building on the corner.

✳ 2 P.M.
WEDNESDAY

"Mr. Patterson!" Barringer burst into the office in a high state of excitement. "I've just had word that Dayton is on fire!"

The NCR president leaped to his feet and looked out

of the big window on the west, but could see no more than a smudge of smoke only slightly darker than the heavy clouds. With his secretary at his heels, he ran for the stairway to the roof. A shiver of horror crawled up Patterson's back as he saw the great flames leaping into the sky from the downtown sector, belching clouds of oily smoke which were blown almost due south toward them on the brisk wind.

"I was afraid of this," he said. "Where do you place it?"

Barringer studied the distant conflagration carefully. "It's hard to say for sure with the wind carrying the smoke this way, but I'm inclined to think it's between Jefferson and St. Clair and in one of the two blocks — or both — bounded by Second and Fourth Streets."

"That's about right, I think. Dear God, this might be a terrible thing. Those buildings are bound to be full of people trapped when the water came up. And the Beckle House is in the next block west, with probably half a thousand people in it alone." Patterson slapped his hand along his trouser leg angrily.

"Is there nothing that can be done to extinguish it, sir?"

The executive was silent for a long while and when at length he spoke, his words were almost inaudible.

"Only one thing," he said. "An act of God. I suggest we pray for a heavy rainfall and the cessation of this wind. Without either, what is left of Dayton now may well be gone tomorrow — and many thousands of lives with it."

✳ 2:25 P.M.

In addition to the Burkhardt and Rotterman Drug
Store building, which was little more than a pile of
rubble when the fire began, five more of the buildings
fronting on East Third Street — Finke Brothers, Johnson and Watson, Evans Brothers, Patterson Tool and
Cooper Saddlery — had now collapsed. In addition, the
five other buildings adjoining to the east, up to the
Beckle Building, which was still in good shape, were
burning savagely.

The roof of the bindery across the alley from Kirkbride's group huddling on the Simms Building was a
full twelve feet away, and as the fire grew behind them,
so grew their panic.

Kirkbride looked for something on the Groneweg
Bindery roof that he could throw a loop over, but the
only thing other than the chimney, which was too far
away on the other side of the roof, was a tall iron vent
pipe that didn't look particularly strong. He quickly
fashioned a noose in the rope, opened it wide and tossed
it across. It missed. Five times in a row he missed, and
then at last the loop settled over the pipe and he drew
it tight.

He jerked on it experimentally and it seemed firm
enough. His own end he anchored high up on a brick
chimney. With his legs twisted about the rope and his
hands gripping it ahead of him, he began moving slowly

across the chasm, his body hanging down. He made
the short trip without difficulty except that he had a bit
of a problem swinging himself up onto the roof.

"For pity's sake," said one of the women, beginning
to cry, "I can't do that. I can't!"

"That's all right, ma'am," said Josh Timmerle. "Now
that he's across safely, we'll figure something out."

It wasn't quite that simple. Kirkbride smashed open
a skylight with the hammer and dropped down into the
building. Almost immediately there was the pounding
of feet running upstairs and two men came into view,
their expressions fearful of some unknown peril awaiting
them here. They stared at Kirkbride in astonishment.

"Didn't know anyone was in here," the bookkeeper
said. "I've got nearly forty people waiting on the roof
across the alley. Got to get 'em over here."

One of the men nodded. "There's more'n fifty of us
down on the second floor. Where'd you come from?"

"On Third Street near Rotterman's. The whole block's
going up and we'll have to get out of here. You people,
too, if you don't want to get caught. Better tell 'em to
get ready while I figure something out for my folks."

Both men clattered downstairs and Kirkbride went to
the alley window and looked out. If the rope was passed
down to here, they might be able to make a sling-slide
for the women and children. To the east in the alley he
could see the Hoover Livery burning brightly, and he
frowned.

Wasting no time, he scaled the wall ladder, opened
the hatch and climbed back out onto the roof. He
shouted to Timmerle to untie the rope from the chimney

and drew it over to himself. Working fast, he cut several sections from the end and knotted them into a square rope seat. To this he attached two other lengths to fit over the slanting rope. It looked sort of like the skeleton of a hammock, but he thought it would work all right. It would *have* to work, he reminded himself.

He called over to Timmerle again, explaining what to do, and then tossed him both the coil of rope and the sling-seat. He returned to the office below and caught the end of the rope when it was thrown to him. Lest any of them be cut, he smashed out the window with his hammer, broke away the window frame and tied his end of the rope firmly to a radiator on the other side of the big room.

"All right," he called, "let's try one of the boys, first."

It was to Timmerle's credit that he positioned his own son in the makeshift seat first, told him all he had to do was hang onto the brace ropes leading from the slanting rope to his seat and Harvey Kirkbride would get him in safely. Sliding the seat to the edge, Timmerle and another man lifted the boy over the cornice, told him to close his eyes and let him go. It couldn't have worked better. Kirkbride caught him as he slid neatly through the window opening and helped him out of the seat. Leaning far out over the alley, he flung the seat back to Timmerle, who snagged it deftly and then said, with a huge grin, "Kirkbride, you're a bloomin' genius!"

They repeated the process then with the other boy, Johnny Beman, the five women and seven of the men who didn't trust themselves to swing down the rope by hand as the others did. The group from below crowded upstairs, and several of the men lent a hand in the operation.

The wind shifted a little now and the alley was becoming filled with thick, choking smoke which led them to believe the fire in the livery barn had now jumped to buildings north of the alley at the east end of the block. If that was the case, it would only be a matter of time until the fire swept this area too.

Kirkbride confidently took over leadership of the expanded group. "Let's get moving," he said. "We've got to get out of this." The other end of the rope was still attached to the chimney of the Simms Building, so he cut it with his pocketknife as far as he could reach out the window. It left them with about thirty-five feet of rope, and Kirkbride asked if there was any rope in the building. One of the men who had first come upstairs told him there was a big coil — maybe a hundred feet — downstairs, and he went to get it.

The cornices were wider here, and it was easier walking. There were two spots as they moved from building to building where the height of the cornices changed, and as each of the women and children cautiously moved past the spot, a man on each end held them snugly against the wall with the rope.

When they reached the Johnson Printing Company at 44 North Jefferson, Kirkbride hoped to find his employer there. Mr. Johnson had often spoken highly of the benefits of having both firms in this single block. The liabilities of such an arrangement, now that fire was consuming the block, were painfully apparent. The man wasn't there, but nearly fifty of his employees were, and they gratefully fell under Kirkbride's leadership.

They descended to the second floor rear and from here could clearly see through the open window that the fire had not, in fact, jumped the alley after all, although more of the larger buildings fronting Third Street had collapsed, and the fire still blazed out of control. The wind had shifted back to the north, and it was this that prevented the fire from leaping the narrow chasm.

To their left were several houses, large old residences fronting on Second Street and easily accessible to them simply by crawling across a ladder they found inside and positioned from sill to shed roof eight feet away. In turn they crept across it to the roof. From there they jumped carefully over the three-foot gaps between shed and garage roofs until they reached the rear second floor window of 118 East Second Street, the office of Dr. G. H. Geiger, a specialist in nervous diseases.

"Now there's the man we've all needed ever since yesterday morning," Timmerle said, keeping a straight face. The comment snapped the tension gripping them all and the sound of their laughter was weird to those marooned in nearby buildings who heard it faintly on the wind.

Heads suddenly appeared at the windows of the doctor's office, but their welcome of the group was not especially enthusiastic. The reason was soon clear. Already eighty people had gathered in the big old house from less safe buildings along Second Street, and with over double the same number seeking entry, might not the old structure collapse? The groaning of its floors and timbers seemed to indicate it was not too far-fetched an idea. It was a decidedly chilling prospect.

✳ 3 P.M.
WEDNESDAY

Dr. John Reeve smiled down at Emma, who was sleeping soundly for the first time since he had carried her up here yesterday morning. He was glad she had managed to drink a full glass of water because she had shown symptoms of dehydration. He wished she had stayed awake long enough to drink some more of the hot coffee, too, since these two cups were the last of it, but if it were a choice, she needed rest the most, and he did not disturb her.

He took the remainder of the wooden box slats he had broken and put them on the small fire in the bedroom fireplace. The room had become smoky due to a partially clogged flue, but the radiant heat seeped right to his bones, and he reveled in the warmth. How lucky that he'd had the builders put in the fireplace. They'd never used it before and he knew Emma had considered it an unnecessary extravagance at the time. Now, however, it had proved its worth beyond any prior expectation.

He sat down at the desk again and sipped his coffee as he gazed at the water sliding past. There could be no doubt about it now, the water was going down some. Perhaps they'd come through this all right after all.

Turning, he picked up his pen and dipped it into the ink pot and resumed the letter to Sidney.

Now 3 p.m. — five hours since I broke off. Water evidently falling. Yesterday at three reached highest. Just cleared the globes of electric lights. Was there when night closed. Now two-thirds of light pole visible. Two currents still rage and swirl and eddy along. One from North Wilkinson, the other from East Third Street, joining forces here. They have swept a long section of board fence and placed it right across this corner, so shielding the corner of this house, so sending one down West Third, the other down South Wilkinson. But for this I don't think I should be writing this now.

I dined on a little hard-boiled egg and a little coffee, black, no sugar, neither attractive nor appetizing. We glory in our fire and just think what a find — a teakettle full of rainwater on bathroom stove and forgotten. Now we can drink. You have to get down to bedrock to appreciate such a find as that.

I have lain down a good deal, slept none, but am very tired. I will sleep better tonight. The noises have all stopped and I can close my eyes with the firm assurance that the house will be standing in the morning. Two men in boat and canoe have passed several times, but did not appear anxious to find out if anyone wanted anything. It rains by times, just to make it more cheerful.

All is still — quiet, desolation and ruin. Your mother is a wonderful woman, not a word of complaint or fear has she uttered, not even one of anxiety . . .

[241]

✻ 4:30 P.M.
WEDNESDAY

Wilcox Hartley, paddling in the rear of the canoe, waved when they rounded the corner of Second and St. Clair Streets and came in sight of the Public Library again. Someone waved back, and Willie grinned at Billy Denton in the front of the boat. Between them on the bottom of the craft were a couple of dozen cans of food and fruit juice they'd taken from the second floor storeroom of the grocery on Second.

"Boy, that Laurie's a pretty one, isn't she?" Willie said. "I'm beginning to think there might be some good aspects about this flood after all. Wait'll she sees this stuff we got."

Young Denton nodded, although he didn't look too happy. Just after volunteering to go with Willie — because he was lighter than any of the other men and the frail craft couldn't take much weight — he'd begun to regret his hastiness. He wasn't a very brave person, he knew, and every inch of the way he'd berated himself mentally for the impulsiveness that had made him volunteer. He wished he could be more like Hartley.

He, too, had been rather captivated by the delicate blond, but it was obvious from her actions that ever since Hartley had been rescued from the tree and brought to the library, Laurie Tomlinson had eyes for no one else. That was the main reason he'd said he would go with Hartley on this crazy excursion, to prove to her he could do anything his contemporary could.

For the first hour or so after the fire began across the street, the eleven of them had crowded at the windows, watching with a fascinated horror. Terrified people crossed the roofs as the blaze spread and shot billows of smoke and flame high into the air. With almost nightmare quality they had watched a man atop the Hoover Livery Stable attempt to leap the alley to the roof of the tobacco warehouse, watched as his body struck the edge of the building and plummeted into the water, watched vainly for him to come up in the torrent rushing westward in the alley. That was when Laurie had burst into tears.

"It's awful, awful, awful!" she sobbed, her voice rising higher on each word and rapidly approaching hysteria. The others had gathered around her and, while Mary Althoff hugged her comfortingly, offered varied reassurances. That was when Willie Hartley's eye had fallen on the Indian canoe made of stretched animal hide which was hanging from the ceiling at the rear of the room. He had snapped his fingers and laughed.

"Laurie," he'd said, "how about something to eat and drink?"

She stared at him in amazement, as did the others, and he pointed at the boat. "I'm going to take that and try to make it to the grocery store in the next block. It's light and maneuverable, so I shouldn't have any trouble."

"No," Mary said, "you shouldn't. It's too dangerous. And besides, that's part of the museum collection. I can't let you do it."

"Begging your pardon, ma'am," he said politely, "but

[243]

we've got to have something. I own a canoe myself and have a lot of experience in it. I'll make out all right."

"But I can't let you take it," the librarian protested. "It belongs to the museum. It's old and weak and might leak. It might even sink right away."

Hartley shook his head. "Looks to be in good shape to me," he said. "And I'm not going to damage it. And what's more important, our survival, or a little old canoe?"

"He's got something there," Robert McKenny said. "We've been up here two days and a night without food or water to say nothing of heat or light. If the lad has experience with canoes, I say we should let him take it and try to find us some supplies."

"You're right, McKenny," Warder said. "Water's down a good bit from the high mark, but at this rate it'll still be four-five more days before it's low enough to walk out of here."

Mary Althoff frowned. "I'm in charge of this building — both library *and* museum — and I can't agree to let you take that boat."

"I think we oughta vote on it," Silas Houghton commented. He raised his right hand. "All those in favor of this boy takin' the canoe for some food an' drink, raise your hands."

All but the librarian, the janitor and Laurie raised their hands and Houghton grunted in a satisfied manner. "I reckon that makes it official," he said.

"I'd better go with you, Willie," Warder said. "You'll need someone to help."

"No," said Hartley, "you're too heavy. The canoe's not big enough."

"Then *I'll* go with you!" Billy Denton seemed as surprised by his own words as anyone else. Hartley looked over his slight figure speculatively and then nodded. "All right, let's get going."

Within ten minutes they were on their way, Willie Hartley in the rear confidently dipping his paddle as he maneuvered against the current and Billy Denton not so competently wielding his paddle in front, trying to look nonchalant about the whole thing and failing miserably. The water gushing past wickedly, the crackle and roar of the flaming buildings nearby, the screams of the people trapped on building tops and in upper windows was almost more than he could bear.

Actually, they had made the trip without any great difficulty. The Indian canoe was like a feather on the water and, though highly unstable, also highly maneuverable. The strength of the young men on their paddles more than overcame the rush of the current.

At the store, Billy held the boat against the building as directed by Hartley, while the latter broke a window out with his paddle and climbed through. There was a wealth of material inside, but room in the canoe for only so much. Into a carton Hartley loaded canned fruits, beans, corn, orange juice and tomato juice.

It was a little difficult getting the box into the canoe safely, but they made it. Far down the block near the corner of Jefferson and Second Street a group of people hanging out of the windows of a large old dwelling were calling to them, but they couldn't make out the words. Hartley answered Denton's questioning look with a shake of his head, climbed into the canoe carefully and they started back.

Apparently it was Laurie who had returned Hartley's wave and now the library windows were crowded. As soon as they passed out of reach of the current traveling west on Second Street, the St. Clair current caught them from behind and boosted them along. As their speed increased, so did Billy Denton's fear. When they were about one hundred feet from the building he attempted to backwater to slow them down, and it caused them to bump a tree gently. Billy shifted his weight too sharply, and instantly the canoe capsized.

Inside the library, Laurie crumpled silently to the floor in a faint. The men groaned in despair, and Mary Althoff bent to help the fallen girl, a feeling of guilt riding her strongly for having let them take the boat. She knew if she'd held firm against it they wouldn't have gone, and now the weight of that responsibility crushed her. She couldn't even force herself to look out the window to see what was happening.

In the water Wilcox Hartley came up sputtering and almost at the same moment was tossed into a tree. He managed to hang on and gradually pulled himself out of the water. His hand touched something he thought at first was a vine and then he realized it was the reins he had used previously to tie himself into this very tree. The irony of it struck him so sharply that he suddenly roared with laughter and nearly lost his grip on the branch. As quickly as it had begun his laughter stopped, and he looked around for Billy Denton.

Immediately upon finding himself in the water, a strange calmness enveloped Denton. What he had worried about all the way had happened, and now he had no further need to worry that it might. He popped to the surface and caught a glimpse of the overturned canoe a dozen yards away just before he was spun around in a dizzying little circle by a small whirlpool at the southwest corner of the library, then shot free to float out onto Third Street and westward from there.

The water was rough, and the crosscurrents pulled him in different directions as he passed the intersection of Third and St. Clair. By the time he was drifting smoothly again, he was passing directly in front of the business places on the south side of Third Street. Swiftly the current whirled him past the Nipgen Company at 136 and he ducked his head just in time to keep from crashing into the small marquee of the Star Theater.

For an instant he had a hand hold on the front of the Irvin-Vinson-Jewell Company, but the current tore him loose. He shot past the Nurrenbrock Shoe Store and began passing the Lowe Brothers Paint Store in the Huston Building at the southwest corner of Third and Jefferson. A dozen yards ahead a huge whirlpool made a frightening sucking noise, and he stretched desperately for a window frame and caught it.

He clung with his body trailing limply in the water, too exhausted to pull himself up. Then he felt his wrists gripped and looked up to find a great bull of a man pulling him in. The man lifted him as one lifts a little child by the wrists and with no greater show of effort.

[247]

He drew the boy into the room and lay him on the floor, where Billy coughed and gagged from the water he had swallowed.

The big man handed him a dry towel and squatted beside him, taking one end of it to rub the boy's hair vigorously. Billy stripped, and toweled himself dry while the big man wrung out his shirt and trousers. The latter watched with a faintly amused expression as Billy got back into the damp clothes. Then he stuck out a huge hand.

"I'm John Mollahan," he said, grinning crookedly and showing large yellowed teeth. "They call me Moose. Welcome to the High-water Hotel, refuge for me and thee and about three hundred others, most of which are up on the roof watching the fire across the street."

✻ 4:50 P.M.
WEDNESDAY

Alma Eberly sat disconsolately on the roof of the house next door to where hers had been. Mostly she was quiet, but occasionally she sobbed brokenheartedly at the loss of her home, which she had watched get tipped to one side and then knocked to little pieces that floated away earlier in the day.

A flash of white in the water just below her caught her attention, and she saw it was a piece of paper caught in a small eddy and going round and round. Curiously she leaned down and caught the soggy sheet on her finger. Carefully she lay it on the roof and straightened it out, discovering that it was a piece of sheet music.

The title of the song was "Alma, Where do You Live?"
For at least the twentieth time since she climbed up
to the neighboring roof, Alma Eberly burst into tears.

✳ 5 P.M.
WEDNESDAY

In the darkening corner bedroom of the big brick residence at Third and Wilkinson Streets, Dr. John Reeve
added a few more lines on the letter to his distant son.

Three-fourths of an hour before he had taken the comforter off the bed and shook it out the window to rid it
of the coating of soot that had fallen on it from the
fireplace. Suddenly he had become dizzy and nearly
pitched from the window, saving himself only by dropping the comforter and grasping the window sash. Disgusted with himself and the weakness of his eighty-seven-
year-old body, he had watched the comforter fall to the
water to be whirled out of sight immediately. Now his
face was haggard and tired as he wrote:

*At 5 p.m. — As if one calamity were not enough, I
have been watching the flames of a fire — the highest,
finest flames I ever saw. A man in a canoe, one of my
former patients — Alfred Swift Frank — says it is east of
Beckle Hotel. Where will it stop? Night is falling. Good
night.*

He dropped his pen and bent his head to the crook of
his arm. I feel so old, he thought. Old and tired and depressed. For the first time truly, I realize that I am a

very old man. I shouldn't rest here. If I fall asleep I'll
get stiff and sore.

But his weariness was too great, and his body relaxed
and he fell into a deep dreamless sleep. An hour later,
cold and stiff, his body aching as he had known it would,
with a hundred little miseries, he roused long enough to
shuffle across the dark room to bed. He kicked off his
shoes and fell into it fully clothed. Even as he pulled
the coverlet over himself, he fell asleep, and now he
rested well, his breathing heavy and even. Beside him
his wife awoke only long enough to feel his presence
there, and in the darkness she smiled and her whisper
was audible only to her own ears as she said, "Thank
you, God, for this man."

Wednesday: 6 P.M.

"I TELL you I am *not* going to spend another night in this tree!" Wilcox Hartley was shouting angrily at Hugh Warder. "Don't worry about whether or not I can get there, you just be ready to haul me in when I do."

"Wait a minute," Warder called. He turned around angrily. "Young fool!" he said. "Liable to get himself drowned, that's what. Well, we'll have to figure out how to nab him when he gets here. Anyone got any ideas?"

"Rope's what we need," Silas Houghton said, "but we sure ain't got none."

"Maybe we could hold someone out the window to catch his hands as he goes by," McKenny suggested, but Mary Althoff shook her head vigorously.

"No," she said. "There's no sense in risking even more lives. We'll have to think of something else."

"But what?" Harvey asked. "There's no rope or nothing we can even use in place of a rope up here, Miss Althoff."

"Yes, there is," she said quietly. She walked to the wall and took down one of the long Sioux Indian spears. She handed it to Warder. "Hold this out the window for him to grab."

Warder took it and shoved his head out the window. "Okay, Willie," he called, "we'll hold the shaft end of this spear as close to the water as we can for you to grab. Now make sure you don't miss. There's no second chance."

Hartley raised thumb and finger in a circle and then climbed down the tree until his body was in the water up to his shoulders and the current pressed him against the trunk. The water was still as cold and the current as strong as it had been when the boat overturned.

He kicked off his shoes, braced his feet against the trunk and pushed himself off, swimming with all his strength against the current while at the same time angling toward the building. His energy was expending itself rapidly, and for an awful moment he thought he wouldn't make it. Then he heard Warder yell and looked up to see the butt end of the spear a foot over the water above him.

He reached up and grabbed it with his right hand, felt that hand slipping and then grabbed the shaft with the other hand. The current bumped him into the side of the building, and at his knee he felt a ledge. Carefully, concentrating on his grip, he drew up his legs until his feet found the ledge and he could raise himself. Standing there, the water was at his knees, and without his grip on the spear he could not have remained there. He rested a moment while Warder above him held onto the other end and Harvey held onto Warder's waist to keep him from being pulled out.

"Draw yourself up the shaft as far as you can, Willie," Warder grunted. "Houghton, you reach out and try to take one of his wrists when he does. McKenny, you the other."

Hartley pulled himself up hand over hand, and when his hands were only an inch from Warder's, he felt his right wrist grasped. He was pulled higher, and then the other wrist was clenched and he was pulled into the room. He lay gasping for breath on the floor and Warder set the spear on end along the wall and began unbuttoning his mackinaw shirt again.

"This," he said mildly, "is getting to be a habit."

✳ 6:55 P.M.
WEDNESDAY

Colonel Charles Zimmerman arrived at NCR just before 7 P.M. He had with him one hundred soldiers armed with rifles and wearing heavy woolen overcoats and knee-high boots. He was shown to Patterson's office immediately, but Patterson was not there, and a clerk went to find him.

The president of the firm was on the roof again, where he was watching the fire. A light rain had begun and the wind was barely a murmur now. The fire seemed to be dying down rapidly, and he was thankful for that. When he returned to his office, the military officer greeted him with marked respect.

"I was told you were doing a fine job in relief here,

sir, but I never imagined any operation as extensive as this. You have my sincere admiration and congratulations."

"Thank you," Patterson said briskly. "Can you tell me what your plans are?"

The officer pulled a rolled paper from his overcoat. "Our chief of staff received directions from the governor, sir, that we were to keep you advised on all matters of general concern and to aid you in any way possible. Also, your orders will be complied with by the soldiery wherever possible. My men are at this moment placing the city of Dayton under martial law by posting these placards at principal gathering places." He handed the rolled paper to Patterson who opened and read it.

BY ORDER OF GOVERNOR JAMES M. COX

The City of Dayton, Ohio, has been placed under Martial Law. By his orders I hereby assume command of troops on duty. The citizens of this city are requested to be of service to the National Guard by remaining in their homes or, if out on business, remain as far away from the flooded district as possible. No sightseers or excursionists will be allowed to disembark in Dayton. The various railroads are requested to assist in enforcement of this measure by refusing the sale of tickets to others than those having the most urgent business in this City of Dayton.

The strictest sanitary regulations will be enforced and citizens are requested to do their utmost to assist in this regard.

Violators of these orders will be promptly arrested and

confined until such time as they can be tried by the proper military tribunal. Thieves, looters, and robbers will be dealt with summarily.

Official   By Orders of:
JOHN W. PATTISON CHARLES X. ZIMMERMAN
CHIEF OF STAFF COLONEL, FIFTH INFANTRY
       COMMANDING OFFICER

"What men do you have with you, Colonel?" Patterson asked, handing back the proclamation.

"Only a handful at present, sir. However, there are a good many guardsmen in this city, and all who can be mustered will fall under my command. I understand that General Wood is here also and when he can be rescued, he will assume command. In the meanwhile, more troops are expected in the next day or two and should be on hand to patrol and keep order by the time the water leaves the streets.

"And now," he continued, "if you don't mind, perhaps you will orient me with your organization here and take me on a tour of the fringe of the flooded area."

❋ 7 P.M.
WEDNESDAY

"There it is again, dear, do you hear it?"

Andrew S. Iddings cocked his head to listen for whatever it was his wife kept hearing, but the only sound that reached him was the gurgle of the waters.

"No," he said slowly. "Nothing more than we've been hearing, at any rate."

The brave kerosene lantern on the drop-leaf table spread a warm yellow glow through the spacious upstairs sitting room and held back the deep black of the night outside their windows. On the mantel a delicate clock gently chimed a sixteen-note quatrain and then bonged seven times. It was a pleasant sound, tending to make one forget the misery beyond these walls.

Iddings walked to the front window and leaned out. A cold wet wind filled with fine rain was blowing and in the faint reflection of the fire to the south of them he could see the water level and was greatly relieved to note that it was still dropping and was probably no more than five feet deep in the street now. Or so it seemed.

"Gone down a good deal, dear," he said, shutting the window and dropping to the mohair settee. "Perhaps by tomorrow it'll be all gone."

"I hope so." She glanced up from her crocheting and smiled. "I'm glad we didn't leave our home. We might easily have been caught by the water and drowned."

Iddings grunted an affirmative, remembering the man who had pounded on their door shortly after seven o'clock yesterday morning, yelled something about the levee breaking and then sprinted off. Iddings wondered where he was now and wished the man would have come in rather than rushing away as he did.

This old native stone house at the southeast corner of First and Jefferson Streets had been built nearly a century ago, and it was just as strong, just as tight as it had been then. He had had no doubt that it would withstand any waters that came, and that it had.

Neither he nor his wife had commented very much about the furniture that they had heard bumping around downstairs last night. It hurt to think about it — the beautiful old spinnet that had belonged to his mother, the fine, rich, upholstered furniture, the leather chairs, the fragile china and crystalware, the cut-glass lamps and the imported Persian rugs — all were certainly ruined now. Things like those could be replaced, he knew, but he worried about his wife, for he knew how much she cherished every item.

Then, during the long night she had reached out and touched his hand and whispered, "Are you awake?" and when he told her he was, she leaned over and kissed his cheek very gently and said, "Of all we have, there is nothing more dear to me than you, Andrew. I can carry on well without any of it, but without you I must falter and fail."

Almost immediately she had fallen asleep, but her words had touched him deeply, and in the darkness the tears had burned in his eyes. Before long he, too, had slept a more peaceful sleep than he had anticipated.

Now he suddenly jerked erect as there was a jarring thud just outside the balcony door on the upstairs porch. An instant later came another, then a third. His wife looked at him over her glasses, and he thought fleetingly that her hearing was still far better than his own had ever been. He strode to the balcony door and opened it and for an instant was badly frightened at the sight of the men.

Raggedly clothed, their hands and faces filthied with soot and grime, their eyes burning like dark coals, three

[257]

of them stood there. He was dismayed when another man jumped from the adjoining roof to the porch balcony and when he was followed by still another. The fear must have shown in his features or in the way he stiffened ever so slightly, for the man in front, a coil of rope over one shoulder, a hammer in his hand and a soggy blanket tied about his middle, smiled disarmingly.

"Sorry to disturb you like this, sir," he said. "We've just come across from the fire block and it's been a little difficult. My name is Kirkbride. J. Harvey Kirkbride."

Iddings cocked his head and repeated the last name. "Of Johnson and Watson Company?" he asked.

Surprised, Kirkbride nodded. "Yes, sir, that's right. Do I know you?"

"Only slightly, at best," Iddings said, smiling. "I've handled some legal matters for Johnson and Watson and I've heard your name. In fact, I'm almost sure Mr. Johnson introduced us several months ago. Excuse me, I'm Andrew Iddings. My offices are in the Reibold Building. I'm an attorney."

"Of course," Kirkbride said, "I remember you now. Good to see you, sir."

Another man dropped to the porch and the book printer tilted his head toward the little group. "There are nine of us, Mr. Iddings. We thought we'd try to reach the Biltmore Hotel on Main Street where the ground's a little higher. We saw your light, the only one we've seen, and thought to ask if perhaps you might have a bit of water to spare us. We're all very thirsty."

"By all means, my friend, you and your companions

are welcome to share whatever we have. And I won't hear of you trying to reach Main Street tonight. Not at all. We have plenty of blankets and coverlets, two beds we aren't using and material to make pallets on the floor for the others. Please, come in, come in."

"Well, that's awfully nice of you, Mr. Iddings," Kirkbride said, as another man leaped to the balcony. "But we're all wet and dirty and —"

"Nonsense!" Iddings interrupted. He looked over his shoulder at his wife, who had risen and was staring uncertainly into the darkness. "We have guests, Mrs. Iddings."

So the nine stayed, accepting with appreciation and no little embarrassment the food and water, dry clothing and bedding provided by the attorney and his wife. Iddings was ravenous for news of what was happening, and Kirkbride told him in detail the story of how they had first been trapped by the flood, then forced to flee the fire.

The book printer puffed with huge enjoyment on the cigar the attorney had given him and told how the 250 or more people who had assembled at Dr. Geiger's place had become frightened at the way the building creaked and groaned, fearing it would collapse with their weight. One of the men swam across Second Street with a rope and anchored it to a telephone pole leaning against a porch of the house on the northeast corner. Thirty-nine of the men had gone across, clinging to the rope, and on the other side had split into three groups — the largest going west to St. Clair and then north to Second to take refuge in Parker Vocational High School, a smaller group crossing Jefferson and working its way toward the big Rike-Kumler Company department store at Second and Main and the final nine, Kirkbride's group, heading north on Jefferson with the idea of making it to the Biltmore Hotel, at First and Main.

"If we can make it to the Biltmore," Kirkbride said, "I may just go right on to Mr. Johnson's house. He lives on Monument just a little way west of Main."

They chatted for a short while longer and then turned in — the Iddings in their own bedroom and the two spare rooms shared by the nine men. They had drawn straws for the beds, and Kirkbride was one of the lucky winners. It had taken more than six hours for them to travel less than three blocks and he was bone weary.

Sleep came almost immediately for the book printer, but not before he muttered a little private prayer — his first in many years.

✱ 8 P.M.
WEDNESDAY

Mrs. Leopold Rauh, resplendent in her fine clothing and heavy fur coat, stamped into the Longfellow School relief station on Salem Avenue with all the delicacy of a Sherman tank. She stared angrily at the huddled groups of refugees on the floor and along the walls, at the crying children and silent men and grieving women.

"Who's in charge here?" she called out at last.

"I guess I am at the moment, ma'am," said a tall

man about forty. "My name is Robert Dexter. Can I help you?"

"Well, I should think so, Mr. Dexter. What's this I hear about the residents of this area refusing to help the refugees. Is this true?"

"Well," he hedged a bit, "it isn't so much that they outrightly refuse to help, it's just that there are so many of them — refugees, I mean — that enough people haven't come in to offer the use of their homes to put them up until the flood's over."

"How many do you have that need shelter?"

"About four hundred right now, but there are more coming in all the time. We haven't very much to offer them here. Do you have room to take some?"

"I have," she said crisply, "if they won't mind sleeping on pallets on the floor. I have plenty of blankets but not many beds."

"Yes, ma'am. How many can you take?"

"I will take fifty. And I'm sure," she added meaningfully, "that I can persuade my neighbors to take the rest."

An hour later the fifty — mostly women and children — were making their own pallets on the floor of the magnificent ballroom of her palatial home. Light from the lanterns about the room glinted cheerfully from the crystals of the massive French chandelier and the cut-glass lamps.

Mrs. Rauh paused at the door and addressed the group. "I'm going out now to check with some of my neighbors," she said, "but I'll be back in a short while. Make yourselves comfortable. I'm afraid the only servant on hand is the cook, who is presently fixing some food for you on an open fire in the back yard."

She bobbed her head and disappeared out the door. A ten-year-old boy stole away from his mother and slipped up the huge staircase. He pulled open drawer after drawer, dumping their contents on the floor, and only when the sound of hammering echoed faintly through the house did his mother realize he was gone.

When she found him — in a beautifully furnished combination sitting room and library, he was methodically pounding large upholstery tacks into Mrs. Leopold Rauh's fine ancestral mahogany. Already the chairs, tables and a magnificent grand piano were studded with them.

✳ 9 P.M.
WEDNESDAY

By this time it appeared to the multitude of frightened refugees on the roof of the Lowe Brothers Paint Store at the southeast corner of Third and Jefferson that the devastating fire across the street would burn itself out. For hours, under the direction of Moose Mollahan, the men had rushed back and forth on the roof tops with mops and brooms, beating out the chunks of blazing material blown across Third Street.

The fire in the buildings fronting on Third Street had devoured all but the big corner Beckle Building, whose twenty-inch fire wall had performed its function well. The rest of the buildings north to the alley, except for those on the east side of Jefferson Street, had been destroyed, and the fire was burning continually lower.

Occasionally there were still minor explosions as containers of volatiles blew up, but at least the blaze seemed destined to die away.

It seemed so, that is, until fate intervened.

A wall of one of the gutted buildings buckled and collapsed, and a large chunk of burning material, catapulted by a snapping beam, lofted through the air in a graceful arc, hit the front of the Nurrenbrock Building on the south side of Third Street and dropped into the water, where it floated, still burning.

As it neared the corner of Third and Jefferson, a little eddy caught it and sent it spinning through the missing window of the Lowe Brothers Paint Store. It drifted to the rear and lodged against a shelf upon which were numerous cans in scattered disarray. One of these had overturned and somehow opened and on the shelf a large pool of paint had oozed. It caught fire right away and burned fiercely around the other cans until there was a muffled blast as one of them exploded and showered the flaming paint all over the store's interior. Now there was no stopping it. In less than five minutes the store was a devilishly crackling conflagration with blast after blast occurring as the containers of paint and turpentine and other volatile fluids blew up.

"Head south, over the roofs!" Mollahan shouted. "Follow me!"

The more than three hundred refugees — including young Billy Denton, whom he'd pulled from the water less than six hours ago — followed the huge man to the roof of the Kette Sons Wholesale Liquor Company, from there to the big Huber Furniture Company and then to the roof of the Western Union Telegraph Building.

Between this and the next structure — the Patterson Building — was a gap of eight feet, and it was also one floor higher. It seemed they were stranded and already great balls of flame were belching through the roof of Lowe Brothers.

The hatch of the Western Union Building was locked, but Moose Mollahan ripped it clean from its hinges with one mighty heave and then dropped himself into the dusty storeroom. He grinned in relief at the sight of a sturdy ladder lying along the wall. Moments later the refugees were scrambling up its rungs to the roof of the Patterson Building. Again — this time with a hand ax when it resisted his tugging — Moose broke open a hatch and disappeared into the building while the others were still coming over. He reappeared a few minutes later and called for some help.

Thirty men followed him back inside and returned with a precious commodity — fire extinguishers taken from the second floor quarters of the Pyrene Fire Extinguisher Company.

Once again the ladder had to be laid across a gap, this time spanning the alley, between the Patterson Building and the office of the *Journal* and *Herald* newspapers at 40 South Jefferson. A total of 317 people, including two blind men, two women on crutches and five other women with babes in their arms, crawled across the makeshift bridge without incident.

On the west side of Jefferson Street, scores of refugees were certain that the growing fire would soon jump to their own block and they began to evacuate. More than a hundred climbed to the roofs of the Hollencamp Building and the Odd Fellows Hall and began the dangerous rooftop walk to the tall Conover Building at the southeast corner of the city's principal intersection.

"I want twenty volunteers with fire extinguishers," Moose roared over the crackle of the fire after all had crossed. He got them. "You men stay on the north side of this roof," he ordered, "while we head for the Beaver Power Building. Try to keep the fire from jumping the alley when it gets here. The rest of you follow me."

Again he led the way, crossing over the wide flat roof of the Weisenborn Livery Stables and thereby by-passing the high roof of the Home Telephone Building. Everywhere the refugees turned, Moose Mollahan was there, urging them on, helping, directing, ordering.

When they had finally broken through a west window into the five-story Beaver Power Building, which took up nearly a quarter of a block from the northwest corner of Fourth and St. Clair, he stood at a window and looked back at the great flames blossoming upward from the whole north half of the block.

"By God," he growled, "it hasn't whipped us yet!"

✳ 10 P.M.
WEDNESDAY

"Oh, Mother, I'm so hungry I could die!" Mary Wallace's nine-year-old lips trembled in an effort not to cry. Seven-year-old Bobbie was not as successful.

"And thirsty!" he added, sniffling.

Little Sarah, four years old, clung wide-eyed in her mother's arms, unable to fully understand what was happening.

Mrs. Clinton Wallace bit her lip nervously and then leaned over to kiss each of the children in turn. She wished Clint were here now — they lived at 3 Zinc Avenue — but, in a way, was glad he had gone out of town. If he'd been here he might have been caught more dangerously in the waters than were they. She listened to the water hissing by less than two feet below their second floor windows and suppressed a shudder. The children mustn't know how terrified she was.

"I think if we have faith in God," she told them gently, "everything'll come out all right. Just think how Daddy must be wondering about us and worried that we're in danger or have been hurt or . . ." She broke off, unwilling to voice the thought. "Come," she said suddenly, "let's all kneel beside the bed here and say a prayer."

She knelt and braced her elbows on the edge of the bed, and the children did the same, except for Sarah, who was too little to get her elbows to the bed when she was kneeling and so bowed her head against the spread.

"Our heavenly Father," the woman began, "for keeping us safe this long in this terrible time, we thank Thee. We pray that You will continue to protect us and extend to Clint Your blessings and keep him safe. We ask for the help of the many people who are trapped by this flood and we also ask Your forgiveness of those who have already perished. This we ask in Thy name."

As usual, the three children added their comments one after another.

"And please, God," Mary said, "send Daddy back to help us soon."

"And send us some food," Sarah added.

"And water," said Bobbie.

"Amen," all of them said.

Just then there was a sharp thump at the corner of the house, and the woman leaped to her feet and ran to the window. She was just in time to see a crate that had bumped the house sliding past along the wall beneath them. Without hesitation she leaned out and caught it, drew it back a little in order to get a better grip on it and then, with some difficulty, pulled it in the window.

Inside were two dozen fine big grapefruits.

"Boy!" said Bobbie wonderingly, "God sure don't fool around when he answers, does he?"

✳ 11 P.M.
WEDNESDAY

The fire spread quickly to both south and east, enveloping in flames every structure from the Patterson Building on the north side of the alley at Jefferson to the Kimmel Seed and Hardware Company at the southwest corner of Third and St. Clair.

Time after time the flames roared across the alley to the roof of the *Journal* and *Herald* Building, driving the firefighters back, but each time they returned with their extinguishers to douse the flames which broke out.

Their hair and brows and eyelashes were singed away, but still they worked.

Meanwhile, Moose Mollahan with a company of over one hundred men crossed the east end of the alley on the ladder from the third floor of the Beaver Power Building to the third floor of the Ball Candy Company. Here they found buckets, hundreds of them, loaded with condiments and candies, citrus fruits and condensed milk. They took every bucket they could find, carrying them back across the alley to their headquarters. Some of them were emptied first, but much of the candy, fruit and canned milk were carried back to feed the assemblage. When they had finished, some 220 empty buckets were piled and stacked on the floor.

"All right," Moose shouted, quieting the hubbub of voices, "if we're going to save ourselves, we've only begun our work." He looked out of the west window and saw that the flames of the Patterson Building had died down and nodded with satisfaction. "Billy!"

Billy Denton stood up and said, "Yes, sir?" and threaded his way through the crowd to Moose.

"Billy, you take a bucket of candy and fruit back to those fire-eaters over there. Send 'em all back here but five. This stuff," he pointed to the bucket, "is for those five. Tell 'em to stay on guard for any more alley-jumping of that fire but to get back over here as soon as it's safe. Got it?"

"Yes, sir, Mr. Mollahan." Billy snatched up a bucket and left. Moose turned back to the crowd. "Now, how many able-bodied men do we have? Looks like . . . uh . . . 'bout 250–275. Good. We're going to need every one of 'em right quick. All of you eat some candy and fruit right now to give you some energy. You'll need it. The condensed milk is for no one except mothers with babies."

He glanced from the window in time to see Billy Denton reach the roof and talk to the men. Most of the party broke away and began the trip across the livery barn roof to this building. He grinned when he saw them coming, but the expression faded when he looked out of the north window.

The interior of the Ball Candy Company was now a roaring inferno.

✳ 11:15 P.M.
WEDNESDAY

John H. Patterson had slept less than four hours since awakening in his own bed at home forty-two hours ago, but right now he was more restless than sleepy. He seemed as omnipresent as a god as he roamed the hallways and rooms of the factory from basement to roof. He was able to tell at a glance how things were going, and he anticipated needs before they were felt. His rescue and relief organization operated as smoothly and efficiently as his manufacture of cash registers did in normal times. He might be seen on the roof, in the hospital, at the garage or in the morgue, all within a ten-minute period, and there were many who openly marveled at his strength and constancy.

Most of the time during the past three or four hours, however, had been spent on the roof, where now a crowd

[269]

of over five hundred had gathered. The fire which had appeared to be dying down earlier in Dayton had abruptly sprung into a roaring conflagration whose flames could be seen easily from here and whose light sent weird patterns of ugly ominous red racing across the undersides of the low clouds overhanging the city.

Great chunks of burning matter went sailing through the air on the freshening wind, and Patterson had little doubt now that the Beckle House must be one of the buildings being ravaged by the fire. In his mind's eye he could picture the awful choice confronting those trapped in the fire's path — either remain where they were and burn to death or leap from the windows and drown. The thought very nearly made him sick.

Hour after hour the fire raged, and even from this distance could be heard the occasional booming of small explosions. As always, wherever he went lately, Patterson was followed by an ever-expanding set of reporters. They were there from Cleveland, Cincinnati, New York, Chicago, Detroit and dozens of other cities. Associated Press alone had eleven reporters on the scene. He would have been wholly justified in ordering them out of his way, but he did not. Instead, he treated them with grave courtesy. They plied him with questions upon questions about the flooding, the rescue work, the relief set-up and even the identity of the bodies which were being brought to the NCR morgue with some regularity now and which, at this time, totaled fifty.

Where he knew the answer, Patterson would give it without hesitation, but where it was a matter of speculation he would refuse to comment, adding that as soon as he found out himself, they would be informed.

Now they clustered about him on the roof. Will all of Dayton burn? Will the fire come this far? Are more soldiers coming? How many people have burned to death already? What buildings are burning? Is the big Beckle House Hotel afire?

He tried to help them all he could but at last he shook his head wearily. "I'm very sorry, gentlemen," he said, "but I really know nothing more about the fire than you yourselves know. I have been no closer to it nor seen any more of it than have you. I can only say the fire is undoubtedly in an area where a great many people are congested. It seems to be burning worst at or very near the Beckle House, where several hundreds of people reside. The hazards of rowing a boat in these flood-waters at night are greatly magnified, but, nonetheless, I have sent out a few of our boats with volunteers to reconnoiter and, if possible, to assist in rescuing those who might be trapped. As soon as I hear from them I shall let you know. And now, gentlemen, if you'll excuse me? I'm suddenly very tired."

They thanked him and watched as he entered the elevator. The closing of the doors broke the spell and they clattered all the way down the stairs to their second floor press room. In short order the typewriters were clicking furiously and then screaming in sharp protest as the sheets were ripped out and rushed away to be telegraphed or telephoned on the newly repaired lines to their newspapers and wire services. Their inaccuracy

was as great as their enthusiasm, and from coast to coast
in this nation — from New York and Chicago and Miami
to San Francisco and Seattle and Tucson — the Thursday morning newspapers greeted their readers with
such sensational headlines as:

SEND DYNAMITE, PLEA OF DAYTON, SWEPT BY FIRE

MARTIAL LAW DECLARED; SOLDIERS PROWL CITY

FIRST DETAILS OF GREAT DISASTER

FLAMES MENACE DAYTON — HUNDREDS FLEE

DEATH ESTIMATE IN DAYTON: 6000 TO 8000!

PEOPLE OBSERVED THROUGH FIELD GLASSES LEAP FROM
FLAMES INTO FLOOD WATERS

ENTIRE NATIONAL GUARD OF OHIO WILL BE RUSHED TO
CITY AS QUICKLY AS POSSIBLE

FLAMES ARE SWEEPING TOWARD BECKLE HOTEL CROWDED
WITH GUESTS

FIRST PROVISIONS ARRIVE AND BOATS BEGIN WORK OF
RELIEF AMONG SUFFERERS

FLAMES WIPE OUT BUSINESS PARTS OF CITY

200 BODIES ARE FOUND IN RAGING WATERS AT DAYTON, OHIO

FLOODED OHIO CITY AFLAME: APPEAL FRANTICALLY FOR AID

TENTH OF CITY'S 130,000 MAY BE DEAD!

FIRES BREAK OUT ANEW AND WORK OF RESCUE STOPS DURING
DARK HOURS

DAYTON, OHIO, IS DOOMED CITY

One reporter — perhaps remembering that great news
story of the sinking of the *Titanic,* which had occurred

only nineteen days short of a year ago — could not resist writing: "Singing was heard across the roaring waters all night as people raised their voices together in such hymns as 'Onward Christian Soldiers' and 'Nearer My God to Thee.'"

To the newspaper readers of the nation at large, Dayton was this week suffering a disaster greater by far than the San Francisco earthquake.

Thursday

✳ 3 A.M.

ALL NIGHT the light of the flames from the fires on both sides of Third Street glowed through the windows of the Public Library, and though several of the group imprisoned there made an attempt to sleep, none met with success. The occasional small explosions of whiskey, paint and kerosene continued at intervals.

Every now and then a wall would collapse and plunge into the water with a great hissing splash. Between two of the west wall windows, Willie Hartley lay with his head in the lap of Laurie Tomlinson, covered with the big buffalo skin. He kept dozing and then waking as another noise sounded outside, only to feel Laurie's warm, wonderfully soft and gently reassuring hand as it stroked his brow and hair.

Just after 3 A.M. there was a louder crash than usual, and Mary Althoff, standing at the window, gasped. The others came crowding around her. Part of the Kimmel

Seed and Hardware Company on the southwest corner
of Third and St. Clair had collapsed. A great blossom
of fire flared up for a few minutes, lighting the sky
more brightly than ever and sending huge burning pieces
of debris floating up and away on the rather brisk wind
from the northeast.

"Thank God that wind's not blowing this way," Mc-
Kenny muttered. "We'd be in trouble if it were."

"We're not safe from it by any means," the librarian
said. "Look there!"

As if to corroborate her words, another floor of the
building collapsed and some of the debris was shot considerable distances, as by a cannon. One of these pieces,
a flaming timber, whirled crazily through the air toward
them but hit the top of a Cooper Park tree where it
lodged and burned for awhile before dropping to the
water. The tree it hit was no more than twenty yards
away.

"No," Mary repeated, "we're not altogether safe from
it."

"Oh-oh," Warder said suddenly, "look over here."

A large chunk of burning matter had lodged on the
cornice of the Gebhart Iron Company building on the
southeast corner of Third and St. Clair. It flickered
brightly, caught hold and soon the roof of this building
was blazing. In a short time, the Ohio Block Building
next door east was burning as well.

"I think," Mary Althoff said slowly, "we had better
post lookouts at each of the windows on all sides of
this building. That way if floating or flying material that

is burning happens to lodge against the library, we may be able to push it off into the water before it sets us afire."

✳ 4 A.M.
THURSDAY

The job was done . . . and the men were done in.

To the north of the Beaver Power Building lay a great smoking ruin of dozens of fine business establishments. The wind had faded to almost nothing now and what flames were visible curled and crackled in a desultory way, seemingly satisfied to consume the bits and pieces of rubble left to it.

Inside the power building was a strange scene. Men everywhere lay panting and gasping on sodden floors, oblivious of the dirty, debris-filled water that soaked them. They were safe now, but only at the cost of a tremendous expenditure of effort that had left them all exhausted. Not a man there had hands which weren't blistered and raw, nor was there one whose back did not ache with an excruciating agony.

The real work that Moose Mollahan had announced was in store for them had begun immediately after the return of the fifteen men from the roof of the *Journal* and *Herald* Building. He had directed them with a relentlessness one might have expected of a prison guard over his chain gang. There was one main difference. No one had worked any harder than Moose Mollahan himself.

It began with the movement of heavy metal machinery

in front of the windows on the north side of the building on all four floors above water. The remainder of the machinery and other equipment was then moved laboriously to the far south walls where it was stacked in cluttered piles. This included boxes and crates, desks and chairs, various machinery and office equipment. It took nearly an hour, with over fifty men working on each floor to do it. By the time they had finished, the Ball Candy Company across the alley was a great torch so hot that the wire-mesh windows in front of which they had stacked machinery melted, sagged and dripped to the floor.

The bucket brigade had formed then, originating midway down the steps to the first floor, with men two feet apart all the way up to the roof. Bucket after bucket of water was dumped on the roof until two inches of water covered the entire expanse, threatening to top the level of the hatch and run back downstairs. A five-man guard was left up there and the line moved to the fifth floor. Once more the buckets of water began to come and were sloshed against the north walls and dumped on the floors. This was repeated on the fourth, third and second floors and though the walls became so hot that the dashing of water against them resulted in clouds of steam, the fire did not gain a toehold in the Beaver Power Building.

There would be no accurate way to say how much water was carried upstairs during these hours, but an estimate of ten thousand pails full would be conservative. The women, the lame, the elderly, the blind, these sat or lay on desks to keep out of the way, and their hearts went out to the men who had worked themselves into a state of nearly total exhaustion. But the job was done, the fire beaten, the flood waters receding.

The work done by these people — none of whom had ever fought a fire in his life — undoubtedly prevented much of the business district of Dayton from burning, to say nothing of the hundreds or thousands of lives thus saved.

It was a job well done.

✳ 6:15 A.M.
THURSDAY

In the past two nights and two days, Edward W. Hanley had noticeably aged. His lips were puffy, his eyes sunken and introspective. A great sorrow filled him.

He had no idea how many fires had been started as a result of gas explosions — gas that would not have exploded had he turned off the supply when the flood began — but he knew they were many.

The night had been a hideous nightmare for him as fires burned throughout the city, casting flickering and, to him, accusing red shadows over everything. Much of downtown, he knew, had been destroyed, and he kept forcing down the inclination to speculate on how many lives had been lost because of the fires . . . because of the explosions . . . because of the gas . . . because, as he viewed it, Ed Hanley had made the wrong decision.

He couldn't know that explosions and terrible fires had occurred at about a dozen locations in the city. Nor could he know that fire damage alone in Dayton would total over $2 million.

But the feeling of guilt rode him heavily, and so it was that with the early light of day, Edward Hanley entered the inky water, took a deep breath and disappeared down the stairwell to the valve room. Five times he reappeared at the surface, gulping great draughts of air into his bursting lungs. The last time he pulled himself from the water and slumped in the corner of an office. The gas was off now. There would be no more explosions. It was a feat of great daring and courage, but it had come just a little late.

No one knew it better than Edward Hanley.

✳ 6:30 A.M.
THURSDAY

J. Harvey Kirkbride's party of nine men left Andrew Iddings's fine old home at 6:30 A.M. Their own clothing had not fully dried during the night, but at least the awful sogginess of the garments was gone, and they were merely damp.

Andrew Iddings had urged them to take with them the clothing that he had supplied for them to wear the evening before, but they refused.

"We do appreciate it, Mr. Iddings," Kirkbride said, "and all the other things you've given us, too. But we're going to have to get back into the water and we'll be all messed up again right away, so we might as well wear our own clothes. Anyway, you've suffered enough dam-

[279]

age downstairs without the loss of the clothing you have up here, too."

And so they had gone and found the water level had dropped even more during the night. Behind them the sky was still billowing with smoke from the burning blocks, but the wind had abated now, and apparently the fire would remain confined. Kirkbride had no doubt this was due in large measure to the layer of snow that had coated everything beginning about 4:30 A.M.

Although this section of downtown at First and Jefferson Streets was closer to the Great Miami River levee than the areas they had fled, it was nonetheless higher, and the water in the streets here was mostly about forty inches deep. The current was still strong, but no longer the fierce torrent it had been and, by joining hands to brace one another, the nine made it safely across Jefferson Street.

Along the walls of the buildings on the south side of First Street between Jefferson and Main the walking was easier as the ground rose slightly, and by the time they had reached the Victoria Theater at the southeast corner of First and Main, the water was just to their knees.

Five of the nine elected to cross First Street here and enter the Biltmore Hotel to wait out the recession of the remainder of the waters there. But from this corner they could see sidewalks clear of water diagonally across the street and midway up the block toward Monument Avenue. In fact, several people were standing on the sidewalk in front of the Peckham Garage and Blacksmith Shop over there.

Kirkbride, with the remaining three men, crossed Main Street and waded north to the garage. They were greeted in a friendly fashion by the knot of survivors there and stood in animated clusters for the better part of an hour — each of them anxious to hear of the experiences of the others. Those at the garage were particularly interested in hearing about what had burned, fearing it had been the Beckle House and all its many guests.

Kirkbride was appalled to see how the northwest tower of Steele High School had collapsed. Somehow the ruin of this venerable old building brought home more sharply to him than anything else had what a devastating blow had struck Dayton.

He was told about other buildings here and there that had exploded or just collapsed due to water pressure and heard soberly the opinion that undoubtedly the waters had so weakened all downtown structures that many more buildings were liable to collapse and were decidedly unsafe.

Herbert Craskall, the smith, spat in the water still gutter high in the street. "Just one thing I'm sure of," he announced. "Dayton ain't worth a damn no more. Not to nobody. And me, I'm sure as hell leaving it just as soon as I can."

More than half of his listeners nodded in agreement.

✳ 9 A.M.
THURSDAY

Just after awakening, Dr. Reeve had heard his name being called from outside and hastened to the window.

Below, hanging to the wall of the building to keep his little boat from being pulled away by the weakening current, was John A. McMahon, a neighbor from a few houses away who had been his patient for many years. He said he had room to take the doctor to a safer place if he wanted to go, but the old physician had merely smiled and thanked him, reminding him that his wife was here, too, and he could not leave her, nor would it be wise to try to get her to safety in that tiny boat.

Disappointed, McMahon had gone away, but not before handing up to the doctor a jug of water and a quart bottle of whiskey. "That's in case you get bitten by a snake, Doc," he said with a laugh.

It was an appreciated gift. The doctor poured a half cupful of the liquor and into this he broke the last raw egg and added a little water. He beat it well with a spoon and, when well blended, fed a little of it to Emma. She liked neither whiskey nor eggs, he knew, but she needed the strength it would provide. The remainder that she would not take he drank himself and instantly felt the warmth of the whiskey bloom in his stomach and issue a wave of energy through him.

After changing the bed sheets and caring as well as possible for his wife's toilet, Dr. Reeves sat down at his desk to resume the letter to Sidney.

Thursday at 9 a.m. — Went to sleep saddened by beating rain against windows and by glare of light from flames up Third Street. And by fact that we had lost our comforter. Natural gas would burn no more. Had a long, sound, refreshing sleep, but was wakened by light streaming in. Jumped up to look upstream and see the fire blazing up, great tongues of flame, the whole block must be burning. That was 3:15 a.m. Another good sleep. Wake at six. Driving snow. All everywhere white where snow could rest. Outside all water, but moving very sluggishly now. Top of fence just visible. No sign of life. All desolation and ruin. I know the meaning of the words now.

The Taylors, next door west, called us. Did we want anything? Yes. Coffee. They made us a pot. By long reaching on both sides we can just get to each other. They sent some sandwiches, too, which we cannot eat and did not want. I had a cup of coffee, then a raw egg beaten up with whiskey and a little water. I was glad to give the T's water, whiskey. I have plenty, thanks to J. A. McMahon. Then, next for fire. Broke up paper boxes with a few thin boxtops. Oh, if I had a hatchet or ax. There are bookshelves plenty. Fuel plenty, but efforts to break and pull show me how feeble I am. I just had to lie down.

He paused for a moment and looked outside again. Already the snow was beginning to melt and the dark clouds appeared on the verge of dumping more rain. A movement far up Third Street caught his eye. It was a boat, with a man rowing and a woman in the stern. He watched them with interest and, as they drew near, he saw them wave at him and motion him to open the window.

As luck would have it, the window stuck. The doctor was panting heavily by the time he had it open, and by then the boat was nearly past. He recognized them as friends of Mary's who lived only a few blocks from his daughter. They called back and forth until it was too much of an effort. They waved a final time and disappeared west on Third Street. Dr. Reeve closed the window, and after regaining his breath a bit, sipped some coffee and continued his writing. His hand was unsteady and the words almost illegible.

Now 9:30 a.m. — Sitting here at window saw rapidly coming from east on Third Street, a boat. Man and woman in stern saluted with hands. Window hard to get up. Just had time to hear the shout, "We're Mr. and Mrs. Penfield," from the man. "Do you want anything?" I said, "No, not much," and they were gone. Now they live a few squares from Mary. I hope they will give her word. Evidently they were imprisoned in doctor's office downtown, just getting home. Our other neighbor, Patterson, is in his office. Mrs. Patterson shut up here. I have drunk a little more hot coffee, but mouth and throat so dry I cannot eat.

A shaft of brilliant sunlight suddenly broke through the clouds and brightened the room greatly. Dr. Reeve turned to look out of the window, and behind him his wife's voice came to him faintly.

"It's like . . . like a promise . . . a promise from God, isn't it?"

He spun around, astonished. "The sunlight? Can you *see* it?" he asked quickly, sitting on the bed beside her. He was sure that a miracle had just happened and she

[284]

had regained her sight, but she shook her head slightly.

"No . . . but I feel like God just smiled and everything's going to be all right again."

✳ 10:30 A.M.
THURSDAY

The snow was still falling lightly and it was very cold when J. Harvey Kirkbride knocked on the front door of his employer's house at 18 West Monument Avenue. The front windows were smashed, the big door buckled and one of the pair of porch pillars hung askew. With an effort, the door was swung open and a tall man with a square-nosed shovel in his hand peered owlishly at Kirkbride through small round spectacles.

"Well for . . . Harvey!"

Kirkbride grinned. The expression on Mr. Johnson's face made the whole trip seem almost worthwhile. He glanced past the man at the shambles of the downstairs. "I'd say you could probably use a hand cleaning up in here, boss."

J. W. Johnson stepped back and waved his employee in but he was still amazed. He looked out at the street before closing the door, as if to assure himself there was still water outside.

"Where did you come from?" he asked. "How did you get here?" Kirkbride started to explain but Johnson cut him off with an upraised hand. "No, wait. Come on upstairs first and get into some clean clothes. Then you can tell me all about it."

Kirkbride followed him and gratefully changed clothes,

telling him as he did so about being trapped at the office, the incidents that followed and, ultimately, the fire that burned the block.

"Both operations are gone then?" he asked thinly.

"No, I don't think so. Johnson and Watson is gone for sure. It burned and collapsed almost right away, but your printing company on Jefferson was safe enough when we went through it, and I'm pretty sure the fire never made it north of the alley."

"You took an awful chance getting here," Johnson remarked, after Kirkbride had finished telling him about leaving the block, staying with the Iddings and eventually getting here. "There were a lot of other, safer places closer by. Why didn't you go to one of them?"

Kirkbride shrugged. "Well, I don't know. I guess I figured you'd want to hear what happened to your companies, that's all."

"You say you and Jess were the only ones who made it to work?"

"That's right."

"What happened to Jess then? He didn't get hurt, did he?"

Kirkbride shook his head. "He's all right. Decided to stay at Dr. Geiger's place. He can't swim and he didn't want to take the chance of crossing Second Street just hanging to the rope."

Johnson put his hand on Kirkbride's shoulder and squeezed. "Well, we'll have a loss, there's no doubt about that. But you don't need to worry about whether you've got a job anymore. You have."

"With no place to work?"

"We have to rebuild," Johnson reminded him. "We'll rebuild together, okay?"

"I'm your man," Kirkbride said.

There was little doubt in Johnson's mind about that.

✳ 11 A.M.
THURSDAY

It was over fifty hours now since those trapped in the Public Library had tasted food or water. Their lips were cracked, the skin of their faces felt tight and the constant clammy cold was a danger of no little concern.

Laurie Tomlinson had been crying, and Wilcox Hartley, unable to do much to help her, said angrily, "My God, how much of this can we take?"

Mary Althoff, after a long silence, smiled at him and the girl. "As much as we have to, Mr. Hartley," she said. "As much as it takes to survive."

A few minutes later a voice hailed them from the east side of the building and the group rushed to the window over there. Two men clad in guardsmen's uniforms were below them in a boat—one a corporal, the other a private. The latter was able to hold the boat against the building without too much effort.

"How you folks up there fixed for food?" the corporal asked.

"Food?" McKenny's voice was a croak. "We haven't had food or water since it began. Are you going to get us out of here?"

"We're not," the soldier answered, "but there'll be

someone here for you later today or early tomorrow. Our job is to get food and drink to those who need it to hold 'em till the rescue boats come."

He dug into a carton and came up with two quart cans of grapefruit juice. "All we got left," he apologized. "Catch." He lofted the cans in turn. Warder caught one, McKenny the other.

"Don't worry now, folks," the corporal called as the private shoved them off. "You'll be out of here pretty soon now. Nothing to worry about."

They opened the cans with Harvey's penknife and passed them around. Mary's throat was so dry and swollen that she took only a sip and passed it on. Knowing now that they would actually be saved soon, she was suddenly terribly, terribly weary.

✳ 11:30 A.M.
THURSDAY

It is now eleven-thirty in the morning, Dr. Reeve wrote. *Sky cleared, sun shining. Can see our yard where uncovered by wreckage. Water all out of front room, but several inches of slime and mud prevent my going to foot of stairs. Furniture piled in heaps in front and toward bay window down office stairs. Back office not yet clear of water. Furniture piled in heaps. Think by night I can get a lamp. Boats pass often now. Have brought food for men in YMCA.*

"Hello, up there. John. John Reeve! Are you up there?"
Dr. Reeve dropped his pen and turned to the window.

Below was his colleague Dr. Gerald Henry, who had offices downtown. The man was in a boat clinging to the metal fence out front. He was a rather overweight individual with a shiny bald head gleaming paradoxically over extremely bushy eyebrows.

"How you making out up there, John?" Henry asked.

"As well as could be expected, Jerry, I guess. It's good to see you're safe. Where did you get the boat?"

"Commandeered it from a couple of youngsters out paddling around for a lark. There's a rescue station set up at Longfellow School on Salem. How about me taking you and Emma there?"

"Hang on a minute and I'll see, Jerry. Be right back."

The doctor turned back to his wife and took her hand. "Sweetheart," he said, "Dr. Henry's below with his boat and has offered to take us over to Dayton View. We could lower you out of the window very gently. Think you're up to it?"

"I never was much of one for boat rides, John," Emma said softly, her voice craking so badly it was difficult to understand her. "I don't think you were either. And I won't have you trying, at your age, to lift me up and lower me into a boat and then maybe having a heart attack because of the exertion. The water's going down all the time, isn't it?"

"Yes."

"Then, dear, if it's all right with you, why don't we just wait it out until we can ride away from here in a wagon?"

"If that's what you prefer, that's what we'll do." The old physician returned to the window and leaned out.

"I don't think she's up to it, Jerry," he called and added with a smile, "and I really don't think I am, either. We appreciate the offer, though. Would you try to get word to Mary and Bob for us? Tell them we'll wait until they can come and get us in their wagon."

"Well, all right, John, if that's what you want." It was obvious that Dr. Henry didn't think they were being very wise. "It may be a couple of days, though, before they can get over here."

"That's all right. We've lasted this long. I guess we'll manage a little longer."

"Your choice. I'll probably see Bob tonight. He's helping out over at the Longfellow relief station. I'll tell him."

"Thank you. And thanks again for stopping."

✳ 3:15 P.M.
THURSDAY

About the time that Lieutenant Walter Leatherman climbed to the roof of the National Cash Register Company with his high-powered binoculars, a door to a storeroom in one of downtown's largest clothing dealers finally gave way, liberating over half a hundred clothing dummies in various stages of dress and undress. They floated serenely out onto the street and were bobbed away in a macabre clutter to the main body of the river where they spread out in ragged file over two blocks long.

Leatherman, surgeon for the 3rd Regiment, ONG, swung his glasses from downtown to the western section of the city, clucking his tongue in sympathy as his gaze centered on the huge bulk of St. Elizabeth Hospital on the other side of the river. At many of the windows he could see people looking out.

He lowered the glasses a little to look at the river itself, and it was just at that moment that a dummy of a man, shirtless but wearing trousers, floated into view.

Leatherman sucked in his breath as he saw it and then watched in horror as the shapes of men and women and children drifted past in regular procession. He stopped watching before the whole number of them had passed, and his hands were shaking, his face pale.

On his way downstairs he stopped in at the press quarters and made a small but momentous announcement. "Gentlemen," he told the reporters, "I've just been on the roof looking through these," he tapped his binoculars. "In less than ten minutes I have seen upwards of forty or more bodies drift past on the river and they're still coming. If this is any indication of the death rate — and I don't see how it can help but be — then our previous guesses of eight thousand to thirteen thousand dead may be a dreadful underestimation."

The press room went wild.

✳ 4:45 P.M.
THURSDAY

Despite her weakness, Emma Reeve refused any longer to stay in bed, and the old doctor helped her walk about the room. They stopped at the window and, with his arm around her back and she clinging closely to him, she gave the appearance of a little girl beside him.

"Tell me what it looks like out there, John," she said.

"It isn't pretty, my dear," he murmured. "But at any rate, it's hopeful. There are men sloshing by in the street now, wearing boots. There is a streetcar on its side in our front yard and a badly smashed grand piano."

There was a dead horse there, too, impaled on the iron picket fence, but he did not tell her. She had always loved horses, and it would only upset her. He shook his head sadly. "It's a terrible sight out there. The mud and debris in the street is just beyond belief. If it's this way all over the city, I can't imagine how they'll ever get it all cleaned up."

The doctor's wife sighed and he looked down at her tenderly. "Back to bed with you, Mrs. Reeve," he said. He kissed her cheek. "We can't have you overdoing it now. If someone comes for us tomorrow, you'll need your strength then."

She nodded and let him lead her back to the bed and helped her in. He sat quietly with her for a little while and then kissed her on the forehead and went back to the desk to add a few more lines to the now rather lengthy letter to Sidney.

Now 4:45 p.m. — Things clearing up. Sky is brighter. Sun shines sometimes. Two offers to take us to Dayton View, one by boat from Dr. Henry, the next from Red Cross. Mother refused to go. Men are walking on the tracks out front. Water just to ankles. Inspect track, I suppose. We have done well enough for food. The Taylors sent in a big piece of bologna, fresh bread, coffee. Mother can eat nothing. Drinks coffee. What we want most is milk for her. At four I stripped and went to lower regions, the office below. There is a shorter word. Got the lamp. Coal oil can gone. Got hatchet. Have cut up the bed slats and have more, so fuel is provided for. All floors below, everything covered with mud, slime, so sticky can hardly get free of it. Such a sight below! Furniture overturned, piled in heaps. Dr. Hudson in Red Cross promised to get word to Mary, as did Dr. Henry . . .

✳ 5 P.M.
THURSDAY

The militiaman in the rowboat reached the Public Library at last. He was very young, and Mary Althoff thought he looked more like a boy playing soldier than an actual guardsman. But the lines of fatigue etched on his face were not boylike, and the blue eyes reflected the sorrow and pain and death they had witnessed during the past three days.

The water in East Third Street along Cooper Park was now only five feet deep and around the library only the last three steps of the outside stairs were still under water. Here and there men waded about, some to their knees, others to their waists or deeper. A number of boats were visible, slowly, painstakingly going from building to building checking for survivors.

Despite this activity, there was a strange quiet prevailing, and men spoke softly, as they would in a funeral parlor. There was little levity and even too great a weariness for much expression of joy at the more rapid recession of the waters now.

The guardsman pulled his boat up so that the bow balanced on the first step out of the water and held there, swaying gently. By the time he got to the front door, the ten refugees still remaining in the building met him there.

The library rooms were a shambles — broken glass, tumbled furniture, swollen, waterlogged books, broken shelves and thick slimy muck over everything. It was the first time Mary had been downstairs since the water left the first floor in early afternoon. The sight of the damage sickened her and she felt like crying.

"I've come to offer transportation to safe ground for anyone here that wants to go," he said. His voice was spiritless, uttering a monotonously repeated phrase. "I must inform you of two things; first, that in some areas which we may have to cross the waters are still very dangerous, and if you accompany me it must be at your own risk and with the full realization that we could be swamped or overturned, and, secondly, that Mr. John Patterson has advised that by late tonight or early tomorrow morning the water will be mostly off the streets and it will be safe to walk if you prefer to wait."

The men murmured among themselves. Mary Althoff felt no little fear about venturing forth in the boat with this young man, and yet the idea of remaining in the building for another night was so repugnant to her that she stepped forward.

"I'll go with you," she said.

The soldier nodded and asked Laurie, "What about you, miss?"

The blond girl looked at Wilcox Hartley and then shook her head. "I think I'll wait until tomorrow when I can walk away."

"Me, too," Willie put in hastily. "For some reason I've taken a great dislike to boats." They smiled at his little joke.

"Well, I'm going," Warder said, helping the librarian into the boat. "Anyone else?"

Silas Houghton elected to go along also but the rest declined, preferring the alternative of walking out on the morrow. Silas sat on the back seat with Mary. Warder got in next, squeezing the young soldier's arm as he did so.

"Son," he said, "looks like you could stand a little rest. Let me take a crack at those oars."

The soldier agreed gratefully.

✻ 6 P.M.
THURSDAY

The act of God that John H. Patterson had prayed for occurred. During the small hours of the morning, as the fire still raged in the downtown sector, a driving snow had fallen, coating every roof and cornice and ledge with a soft blanket of white. Time after time large pieces of burning matter sailed through the air to land on roofs as far as a block away, only to burn feebly for a little while and then hiss and die in the melting snow. Other chunks fell into the flooded streets and alleys and immediately went out. Without both the snow and water, the city would almost certainly have been leveled by the blaze.

The snow served another purpose as well. For thousands of persons trapped in upper floors of buildings, on roofs and similar places, the snow was moisture for their parched throats, and they eagerly crammed handfuls into their mouths where it melted in a delicious cold wetness. Many scooped up all they could reach and put it into containers to melt and provide a more lasting supply of drinking water.

All day long the rescuing had continued. Patterson stopped the building of boats at the factory when a total of two hundred of the ungainly craft had been finished by mid-morning, and throughout the remainder of the day each of these boats brought in dozens of refugees. By evening over 4600 people had been taken to dry land, most of whom had gravitated to NCR to enjoy their first taste of food and hot coffee, their first change of clothing and bathing facilities and comfortable beds, their first electric light and heat and running water in some sixty hours. It was a heaven in the midst of hell.

By late evening the water level had dropped considerably, and Patterson predicted confidently that any persons who had not been rescued by boat that day would be able to walk out tomorrow at no greater discomfort than wet and muddy feet could bring.

For the reporters it was somewhat of a disappointment, but there were still a few exciting news stories to be written — here and there a family perched on a roof and still unnoticed by rescuers, a number of aged people developing severe cases of pneumonia, a minor uprising among the prisoners at the workhouse, the finding of bodies here and there, the hunger of the rescued, the possibility of typhoid and diphtheria and other contagious diseases — and they made the most of it in their stories. Again these stories flashed around the nation topped with such headlines as:

DISEASE IS NOW FEARED IN OHIO CITY UNDER WATER

CITIZENS OF STRICKEN CITY GO TO HOUSETOPS

40 DEAD BODIES COUNTED FLOATING DOWN RIVER IN 10 MINUTES: TOLL MAY HIT 15,000

"FOOD AND WATER!" CRY SUFFERERS IN DAYTON

FAMINE FOLLOWS FIRE AND FLOODS IN DAYTON: THOUSANDS MAY STARVE

DIG BODIES OF DAYTON DEAD FROM THE MUD

PRISONERS REVOLT AND THREATEN DEATH TO KEEPER

BABIES BORN IN MIDST OF AWFUL PRIVATION

CONDITIONS HORRIBLE IN DAYTON

DEAD IN DAYTON ESTIMATED AT FROM 800 TO 1500 BY MEN WHO HAVE PENETRATED TO REMOTE PORTIONS OF FLOODED DISTRICT

DECOMPOSING HUMAN CORPSES AND CARCASSES OF ANIMALS ADDING TO DANGER HOVERING OVER DAYTON

DYPHTHERIA PLAGUE RAVAGES CITY

✳ 6:45 P.M.
THURSDAY

Her brother's house had not been touched by the flood. The highest waters had been a full eight blocks distant. Mary Althoff breathed out a great sigh of relief. Though she knew it was impossible, she had almost convinced herself that by the time she got there it would have been swept away or heavily damaged. Lantern light showed through the curtains and she smiled. I'd forgotten, she thought, how homey and wonderful the light of a lantern can be.

She walked up the steps slowly and tapped on the front door. In a moment it was opened by a man in his late twenties. His eyes widened incredulously.

"Mary!"

"Hi, little brother."

"Mary, it's really you!" He flung the door wide and swept her up in a great hug. "We thought . . . we thought . . ."

She nodded and kissed his cheek. "I know, dear. I'm tired and thirsty, but otherwise all right." She held him at arm's length and her eyes narrowed. "You said 'We,'" she said. "Did you mean — " She paused, unable to find the words.

He grinned and called over his shoulder, "Mother! Dad! Mary's here. She's all right!"

The tears came to her then and, interspersed with them, a short heartfelt prayer.

"Thank you, God," she murmured. "Oh, thank you!"

✻ 9 P.M.
THURSDAY

Those rescued by boat came in slowly at first, one here, one there, another elsewhere. But gradually, as the waters receded, as the currents slowed, as the danger from whirlpools and floating debris grew less, the rescues became more frequent. Boats came in with not just one but two, three or four, sometimes even six refugees — miserably cold, hungry, thirsty and afraid.

Many of them had seen their families, their friends, their neighbors swept away before their eyes, had heard the screams and shouts of the anguished. In the sunken wells that were their eyes was mirrored the suffering they had experienced, and their faces were the faces of soldiers who have witnessed brutal combat.

At each place where the water gave way to dry ground on a main thoroughfare there was a rescue station, and as the boats came in to disgorge their pitiful occupants in the lantern light, the crowds standing there surged forward to see if this time — oh, God, make it this time! — the missing loved one was among the rescued. There were cries and wails and happy reunions and the constant cry of "Gangway! Rescue! Give us room!" as the saved were taken to the relief stations and helped into rooms where their wet and dirty clothing was taken and new clothing given them, along with steaming bowls of thick soup and mugs of coffee and wonderful sandwiches.

And always at the edge of each crowd there were those who stood and waited vainly, and for those there were no tears but an overwhelming emptiness that threatened to engulf them.

Friday

✳ 8 A.M.

THE STORIES of Dayton's plight continued to flash across the nation and take front page prominence in most newspapers. Even before the waters had crested, relief in the form of foodstuffs and clothing, money and men was being collected and sent by whatever means possible to Dayton.

The first aid came, of course, from the city's nearest neighbors, who sent many thousands of dollars' worth of equipment and supplies and, most important, able-bodied men to aid in the rescue work. Every town within a hundred miles of the city, not itself in the grip of flood conditions, sent aid. Automobiles, trucks and farmer's wagons brought relief before railroad cars could get through. Twenty-seven relief stations were established at different sectors of the city to collect and distribute the goods as they came in. And the national government acted nearly as promptly.

Rations for a half million people were speedily on the

way from the War Department at the express order of President Woodrow Wilson. The Red Cross collected money by the tens of thousands of dollars and would spend $1.6 million in Dayton for the relief of ten thousand homeless families.

Such relief kept coming in for many weeks, but the amount of supplies and funds collected and contributed within the first hour, the first day and the first week of the Dayton flood was astounding. In fifteen minutes after hearing the news, Hagerstown, Indiana, collected $1500 and sent it to Dayton. The Springfield, Ohio, Masonic Lodge collected $2500 within a half hour and the twenty-five-mile distant city sent six truckloads of men and supplies, followed by twenty-five railroad carloads of goods.

Cincinnati, itself beset by serious flooding, sent $35,000 and ten carloads of provisions. Louisville, Kentucky, on the Ohio River, sent its famed U.S. Life Saving Crew. The littler cities of Eaton and Arcanum and Upper Sandusky sent $4000, $3600 and $2000 respectively, and, just across the Indiana border to the west, Richmond sent $4000. Toledo sent not only $82,000 in cash, but 125 cases of condensed milk, three carloads of provisions, one of clothing, nine flatboats and sixty-two Naval reserve men.

By then the relief from more distant areas began coming in. Detroit sent $15,000 first, then another $50,000, along with a promise of more than $100,000 additional for Dayton's use. New York City sent $175,000, Boston contributed $83,000 and San Francisco, on the first day of hearing about the flood, sent $10,000.

The news affected the whole country. In Salt Lake City, Sarah Bernhardt gave a benefit performance, with the proceeds going to Dayton, and then herself sold newspapers on the streetcorner to encourage contributions. Yakima Valley, Washington, sent nineteen carloads of perishable foodstuffs and the B. F. Goodrich Company sent a full carload of rubber boots and auto tires. Even as far away as Alaska the news brought immediate response, and a check for $92.42 came from Skagway.

Ohio authorities contributed $430,000, and individual contributions from all over North America and many overseas nations totaled $129,700.

All in all, more than $2 million was sent to Dayton, and the donations were deeply appreciated. Yet, despite the generosity, such donations barely scraped the surface of Dayton's loss, which would total well over $300 million!

✳ 9:15 A.M.
FRIDAY

Dr. John Charles Reeve sat at his desk, glancing over the pages of the letter he had written. He had not slept much during the night and a great weight of depression and discouragement had settled over him. He was shocked at the manner in which his handwriting had degenerated over the days since the letter had been started. At first it was strong and smoothly flowing, written in neat, precise lines, but gradually it had become shaky and weak and uneven. It had become an effort even to move the pen across the paper, and the weight of his years crowded down on him suffocatingly.

He looked over at the bed where Emma lay sleeping and was thankful she had finally fallen off. Emma, too, had changed in these few days. Her normally serene face was deeply lined and he knew she was concerned about his health, just as he was about hers. Last night in bed she had run her fingers lightly along his arm and ribs and neck when she had thought he was asleep and he had heard her murmur something so softly he couldn't make it out, and then she had cried quietly before dropping off to sleep.

The physician felt tears well in his own eyes now, and he took off his spectacles and scrubbed at his face with the damp end of a towel, then replaced the glasses on his nose. From the desk drawer he removed a fresh sheet of paper, and in his frail hand wrote *Page Seven* at the top. He couldn't remember when he'd ever written a letter this long.

Friday 9:15 a.m. — Third night passed, fourth day dawned. My toilet; rub face with wet end of towel. Great disappointment last night. Lamp that I made such a perilous trip to get would not burn. Could not sleep. Thoughts of this tragedy on us and others in the city of Dayton kept me awake hours. This morning shows streets and sidewalks clear . . .

* 10 A.M.
FRIDAY

Throughout Thursday night a steady stream of refugees had drifted to NCR until even its spacious quarters were filled and makeshift sleeping pallets were placed on hallway floors and under desks as well as on top of them. The building was a focal center for a wide range of emotions. There were those who never ceased crying and others who remained brightly cheerful despite having undergone severe hardships. Many stood at the windows and watched the continuing procession of oncoming refugees, hoping perhaps to catch a glimpse of a loved one or neighbor. A certain number sat on their cots or pallets or leaned against the walls and just stared into space, remembering the dear faces they would never see again. There were instances when individuals cracked under the strain and had rushed about madly, screaming or cursing, bowling over those in their way and fighting the guards who rushed to subdue them. A few overcame it, but most didn't, and eventually these were taken to the Dayton State Hospital on Wayne Avenue near Stewart Street.

By the first light of day, a wonderful sight met the eyes of all — the water was gone. Here and there in very low places there were still pools of it, but the streets were mostly clear, and Dayton was no longer a Venice gone mad.

The city was an appalling sight. In addition to the

rubble of the buildings that had collapsed or exploded or burned, there was an incredible litter. Everything seemed damaged to some extent. Houses stood one atop the other or tilted to one side or squashed and buckled. Every vehicle in the flood zone was ruined. A thick layer of mud coated the city, and every window of every store was smashed. Poles and wires lay helter-skelter and everywhere one looked were the bodies of horses — of which nearly 1500 lay in the streets.

A special train arrived from Toledo carrying lifeboats and fifty men from the Naval Reserve training ship *Essex* in Lake Erie, under the command of Captain Anthony Nicklett. The sailors peered expectantly out of the windows as the train entered Dayton from the north and gradually their expressions changed to disbelief and then disappointment.

"I'll be damned!" exploded a big red-haired sailor. "Where in hell's all that water we heard about?"

Only a day earlier they would have been a godsend, but now it was a futile, if appreciated, arrival. Under the directions of Captain Nicklett they morosely unloaded their boats and launched them in the Miami River, where for several days they rowed up and down the length of Dayton looking for something to do. At length the boats were pulled out, reloaded on the train and the company returned to the *Essex*.

As they chugged out of the city, the same red-headed sailor seemed to voice the sentiments of the entire company when he slouched in his seat, pulled his hat over his eyes, frowned and said bitterly, "Aw, hell!"

✳ 11 A.M.
FRIDAY

It is now eleven in the morning, Dr. John Reeve wrote, *and have talked with friends in the street. A man from next door got in by ladder from roof to window. He has knocked bookshelves apart for us. Dr. Evans has brought from depot a bucket of coal, so we are well off. Mrs. Patterson has given us bouillon cubes and next door gave us evaporated milk. Mother will not drink it. She ought not put solid food in her stomach. Throws up everything. Drinks the bouillon. I have been downstairs. No imagination can depict the ruin, the wreck. Mud, sticky mud, pulls rubbers from feet. Piano overturned, everything ruined and upset. Sun shining now. Glorious! I tripped on way down to get water. I only just got back. Dropped on floor and lay a good while before I could get up . . .*

A wave of dizziness and nausea flooded the old doctor and for a long time he could write no further.

✳ 12:45 P.M.
FRIDAY

The woman, disheveled, filthy dirty, her clothing in tatters, had crawled and dug about the pile of debris near the corner of Warren and Burns ever since the water had receded. Attempts to coax her away resulted only in rising hysteria on her part, and when one guardsman attempted to force her away with him, she struck him with a board and threatened to kill him if he tried to stop her, so he simply shrugged and rubbed his head and went about his business.

She chanted as she searched and dug, and it was a macabre jingle she sang: "My baby's here...I know she is... My baby's here...she's only three... My baby's here...my baby's here... Oh God, I *know* my baby's here..."

And then, at quarter to one in the afternoon she uncovered the tiny arm of a child, and the shrill scream that erupted from her throat brought men on the run from a block in every direction. She stood with her torn and dirty fingers in her mouth, watching, as the men dug away the debris and freed the body. The baby was nude and badly mutilated and about three years old — but it was a boy, not a girl.

They put the child's body into a wagon to take it to the NCR morgue, and tried to get her to come along, but she jerked away and rushed back to where she had been digging and once more began burrowing through the pile.

"My baby's here...I know she is... My baby's here ...she's only three..."

✳ 2 P.M.
FRIDAY

Former city councilman George W. Miller and his wife, Gertrude, finished shoveling out the remainder of the mud, broken glass and debris from inside their grocery store at 400 North Main Street.

All of the perishables had been destroyed or were unfit for consumption, but there were still great piles of canned goods on the floor and, surprisingly, many shelves full of tins that seemed hardly touched by the rampaging waters.

Miller took the big white door that had been torn from its hinges and propped it up out in front of the store. With a brush dipped in a pot of black paint, he carefully began lettering on the door. It took a good time to finish, and when it was done he stood back and looked at his handiwork critically.

Gertrude came out about that time and looked at it with him. Miller grinned sheepishly. "We weren't able to do much to help in rescuing people," he said, "but maybe this'll help 'em get back on their feet."

Gertrude Miller took her husband's cheeks in her hands and kissed him gently on the lips. "In case I haven't told you lately, I'm awfully glad I'm Mrs. George Miller."

They walked inside the store with their arms about one another's waists and waited for the first customers. Outside, the sign read:

GENERAL INVITATION TO ALL THOSE STRICKEN BY THE FLOOD — COME IN AND HELP YOURSELVES TO ANYTHING YOU MAY NEED. NO CHARGE.

G. MILLER, PROP.

✱ 3:30 P.M.

Robert Ellison Crandler was greatly concerned about his collection of Gramophone records. His, he knew, was one of the largest and finest such collections in the city, and when the rising water had forced him to flee his house, it had been before he had had opportunity to carry the thick discs to safety.

Now, when he returned to his house for the first time since being driven away from it, he was dismayed to find the room a terrible shambles and the records a great pile of broken shards amid the mud and debris.

After going through all two hundred of them, he found only one that was not damaged in some way. Eagerly he looked at the label.

It was a Paul Whiteman piece entitled "Then You'll Remember Me."

✱ 5 P.M.

Evening is approaching, Dr. Reeve wrote. *I cannot write much today. Have had fire all day and natural gas promised for tomorrow. Wish you could see me. Went with great difficulty to kitchen pump for water. I was just reaching the stairs when a narrow board under my foot turned and I went down into the slime. You should see my clothes. Am faint. Mouth, throat so dry I cannot eat. Streets full of people. Have just had word that your brother Charlie is at Lebanon, south of us, at hotel. Am told that our city is under martial law. See lots of badges on street. But how fine is the sunshine all day. Mother keeps about on her feet. How she lives I cannot imagine. She eats so little and then she throws that up.*

He stopped writing at a loud thumping from downstairs. Someone was at the front door and he called "Come in," but his voice was so weak that he knew whoever it was could not possibly have heard him.

He stood up and started toward the stairs, but a darkness began closing over him, and he barely managed to slump onto a straightback chair near the bedroom door.

Vaguely, as if from some great distance, he heard the door open and a voice calling and then the sound of heavy feet thudding up the stairs.

Saturday

✽ 6 A.M.

THERE MAY have been some justification for inaccuracies in national news stories about Dayton while the flood waters raged, but in its fifth day of front page prominence, when all the flooding was past, the stories were scarcely any more accurate. Of course, what they lacked in accuracy they more than made up for in drama and interest, and that, in the minds of many reporters, justified their embellishments.

After sunset, ran one reporter's story, representative of the majority of reports, *the great buildings, some of which are in ruins, towered darkly and silently into all sorts of weird shapes. The sadness and melancholy inspired by the idea of a deserted village expand into a very real sort of terror when it is a flood-swept city after nightfall without a light within miles that surround you. Half-hysterical and inexperienced national guardsmen, well meaning and honest, patrol the streets in inky blackness, confessedly in terror of being murdered by thieves attracted by the lure of valuable loot. Straying beyond their prescribed beats, they almost shoot one another in an excess of panic. They prod their own officers with bayonets and challenge everyone who passes, even in the middle of the street, with an intensity and ferociousness which betrays their open fear. Shots sound every few minutes from points only a block or two away. There is nothing but blackness and streets pitted with holes and peeled of pavements, as mankind peels its breakfast orange, and silence, save for the sound of rushing water in the distance. The wreck of a large automobile, wheels in the air, looms close at hand, capped by a crown of miscellaneous debris. A steel trolley pole snapped off at the curb is an obstruction underfoot. Walls seem to be leaning and in imminent peril of falling. Gun muzzles are pointed by guards who know no better. Shadows furnish shelter for possible desperadoes. The whole city is terrible and strange.*

✳ 10 A.M.
SATURDAY

Dr. John Charles Reeve lay propped up in bed, the fresh clean linens feeling wonderfully good against his skin, his own body clean as well and smelling nicely of soap and powder. In the bed beside him, Emma lay sleeping peacefully, as clean and as comfortable as himself. He smiled and, propping a book against his knee as a desk, concluded the letter begun an eon ago to his son Sidney in New York State.

Saturday 10 a.m. — Soon after I wrote last, Robert came with a wagon to take us to Dayton View. I got downstairs, but had to be lifted into the wagon. Dr. Henry fortunately came at the same time, and he carried Mother down and over the slimy slippery steps. We rode, my head lying upon a young woman's lap. Mother's was in another. Water too deep in places for a carriage, but we got here safely. Oh, the luxury of washing face and neck and of hot milk!

Dayton View is a huge relief station. Schoolhouse headquarters full and more coming. Good organization. Military. No going about without a pass.

Our rescue came none too soon. I feel certain that I could not have gotten through another night. I have for memory the recollection of a great calamity, second perhaps to the Titanic, but to none other.

With love to all,
Father

✳ 10:15 A.M.
SATURDAY

Martial law had transferred smoothly to the command of General George H. Wood at NCR shortly after he was deposited on Fairgrounds Hill by an NCR boatman. He approved of what Colonel Zimmerman had done to this point, conferred at length with Governor Cox via telephone and with John Patterson in person and then set about posting a series of new orders.

The first of these was an order calling for all inactive

national guardsmen in the area to report immediately at NCR to help with patrols, guard duty, enforcement of regulations and general reconstruction.

The second was an official proclamation confirming what the governor had already told Patterson personally. It read:

DAYTON, OHIO — MARCH 27, 1913 — OHIO NATIONAL GUARD HEADQUARTERS.

MR. JOHN H. PATTERSON, PRESIDENT OF THE NATIONAL CASH REGISTER COMPANY, IS HEREBY APPOINTED PRESIDENT OF THE CITIZEN'S RELIEF COMMITTEE. ALL ORDERS SIGNED BY HIM WILL BE HONORED BY ALL POSTS OF THE OHIO NATIONAL GUARD.

BY ORDER OF JAMES M. COX

GEORGE H. WOOD ADJ. GEN.

Another order protected city merchants by directing that:

NO PERSON NOT A MERCHANT OF DAYTON ON THE 25TH OF MARCH, 1913, MAY OPEN A NEW RETAIL STORE WITHIN THE DISTRICT GOVERNED BY MARTIAL LAW DURING ITS CONTINUANCE WITHOUT FIRST OBTAINING A PERMIT TO DO SO FROM THIS OFFICE. NO EXPENSE WILL BE ATTACHED TO THE ISSUANCE OF SUCH A PERMIT, NO FEE CHARGED, BUT NO SUCH PERMIT WILL BE ISSUED WITHOUT THE MOST SEARCHING INVESTIGATION INTO THE GOOD FAITH AND PERMANENT CHARACTER OF THE PROPOSED NEW ENTERPRISE.

The arrival on Friday of five hundred soldiers each from the 6th Regiment of Toledo and the 2nd Regiment of Lima, along with the remaining four hundred men of Zimmerman's 5th Regiment from Columbus and the Dayton National Guardsmen swelled the militia under General Wood to over two thousand men and permitted him to establish more stringent regulations, one of which was a curfew.

CURFEW WILL BE SOUNDED BEGINNING AT 6 P.M. TODAY BY THE RINGING OF BELLS ON CHURCHES. ALL CITIZENS MUST KEEP OFF THE STREETS FROM THAT TIME UNTIL 5 A.M. THOSE DISOBEYING THIS WILL NOT ONLY BE SUBJECT TO ARREST BUT RUN GREAT DANGER OF BEING SHOT BY GUARDS.

GEORGE H. WOOD, BRIG. GEN.

COMMANDING

This order gave newsmen the raw material for some very exciting stories with an equivalent degree of accuracy as that in many of their previous reports. Some of the stories were pure fiction, such as the one which appeared in the Cincinnati *Enquirer*, which was the prototype of similar tales appearing in newspapers throughout the nation. It said:

Seventeen men have been shot and killed in the streets of Dayton, as looters, since the declaration of martial law. Ten were killed between darkness last night and light this morning. Nine were Negroes and the tenth a white man. The only white man was 17 years old and his crimes brought instant death. After the curfew bells tolled at 6 p.m. last night, the orders were to shoot to kill all persons in the business district who refused to answer the hails of National Guardsmen. Shortly after

[315]

2 a.m. today, the sentry on post at Third and Main halted a young white man whom he discovered in the deep shadows along the unlighted street. He called upon him to advance and the man stepped forward and displayed on his left arm the brazier of the Red Cross. He said he was a physician and on an urgent call to a dying woman. He kept one hand behind him and the guard told him to extend it. He did so and was holding two gold watches. The guard called for the corporal of the guard. They searched his pockets and found sixteen more watches. The man was led to the steps of the First National Bank building, told to stand on the second step facing the entrance to the building. The corporal posted himself behind, gave the commands to the firing squad and six shots were fired at the man, who crumpled up on the steps. His body rolled to the sidewalk. Later it was removed and disposed of. Adjutant General George H. Wood, in command of the troops, admitted today that there were squad and individual shootings during the night but that no reports of anyone being killed by a sentry had come to him. He admitted that such a report might not have yet reached him.

It was a fascinating story, eagerly devoured by readers. When General Wood heard of it he grew furious and announced publicly that reports of the militia shooting citizens were wild dreams and irresponsible reports. "No person," he said, his deeply lined face very stern, "has been fired upon by any soldier in this city. Such stories are outright falsifications and serve no good purpose."

He was wrong on that last point, however, since they did help to discourage a great many would-be looters and sightseers from coming to the city . . . and there were more than enough who came anyway.

❋ 10:30 A.M.
SATURDAY

"Run for the hills! Run! The Lewistown Reservoir has broken. There's a fifty-foot wall of water coming. *Run!*"

The fearful alarm raced with wildfire speed from Hickory Street south through all of the residential district of South Park — which up until this time had suffered not at all with water damage. But if the reservoir had truly broken . . .!

Within minutes the streets were choked with people fleeing, calling to others who came to their porches or windows the same message that had come to them: "Run for your lives! The reservoir has broken!"

In one of the strangest sights ever seen in Dayton, a full twenty-five thousand people ran frantically to the south, not stopping until they reached the high ground, milling about here where they would be safe and watching for the wall of water to cascade through the city.

Hours later, almost reluctantly, the group broke up and people returned to their homes much more slowly than they had left them — a bit chagrined at first, then deeply angered when some of them discovered that while they had fled their homes had been ransacked of all valuables.

✻ NOON
SATURDAY

At precisely noon, one hour after returning to the factory from their extensive tour of inspection in a motorcade of big powerful touring cars, Dayton civic leaders and the military called their meeting to order in a session closed to reporters and the public.

General George Wood opened the meeting by reading a telegram he had just received from Governor Cox. It commented to some degree on the disaster and how Dayton had withstood it, the aid that had already been sent and would still be forthcoming. It concluded with a ringing accolade for John H. Patterson.

"Mr. Patterson," Wood read, "is entitled to the highest possible credit. The whole state is speaking in praise of his work."

The more than fifty officials in attendance cheered at this and gave Patterson a standing ovation lasting for a full three minutes. Patterson smiled slightly but seemed rather more embarrassed than anything else over the tribute. He shook his head and held up a hand until the voices and applause quieted.

"Whatever credit is due, is due not to me but to the many hundreds of workers who have labored endless hours since last Tuesday to bring relief to the suffering and homeless. No one man can be lifted above any other for his part in this work, for each gave of his utmost, many even dropping from sheer exhaustion before they would quit. To them belongs the credit."

"None of us here," said George Burba, rising, "would attempt to make light of the work done by any of the men in this vast relief organization, but the fact remains that if it wasn't for the inspired foresight of one man — you, Mr. Patterson — this disaster would very likely have had a far more sorrowful complexion. It was your foresight that saw the flood coming. It was your foresight that turned this factory and all its executives and employees into one vast relief and rescue organization in a matter of minutes. It was your foresight that provided boats when they were most needed as well as food and warmth and shelter for all who needed it."

"Well, indeed!" said Patterson. "And why shouldn't we have been ready? If a river is rapidly getting more water than it can hold, isn't it bound to overflow? If the topography of the country is such that the easiest place for an overflow is right into town, why then should a flood like this be such a surprise? If you start a rock rolling down a steep hill, is it a matter of any great surprise if it reaches the bottom?"

The room was silent as these men saw John H. Patterson for the first time as the man his executives knew him to be; a man impatient with praise he felt undeserved and a man who chose always not to dwell on past achievements but rather on future needs.

Patterson looked around the room as if measuring the men there and then he said, "Now what are we going to do about Dayton?"

General Wood cleared his throat a bit self-consciously and said, "Governor Cox has already named you president of the Citizen's Relief Organization and he has advised me that he would consider it a personal favor if you would accept the position of chairman of a Citizen's Relief Committee to determine what Dayton needs and what it must do. This committee is to be comprised of five able men, including yourself, the other four of your choosing. Will you accept?"

"I will," said Patterson without hesitation. "The men I would choose are gathered here today and I will ask them now if they will accept. First, Dayton's mayor, Mr. Edward Phillips."

"Yes," answered Phillips.

"Frank T. Huffman?"

The president of the David Sewing Machine Company nodded and said, "Of course."

"John R. Flotron?"

"Yes," said the president of the John Rouzer Company.

"Finally," Patterson said, "Mr. Adam Schantz, president of the A. Schantz Company. Adam?"

"By all means," Schantz said.

"The Citizen's Relief Committee is hereby formed, General."

Wood was visibly taken aback at the speed with which Patterson got things moving. He nodded approvingly. "Very good. Is there anything you care to say at this moment, sir?"

"There is. Our first task must be to assure that such a disaster as this may never again strike Dayton. The city is still in desperate need of supplies — particularly medical, food and water. I have received word that the special relief train that left New York City for Dayton on Wednesday has arrived. It was routed first to Detroit, southwest to Toledo, southeast to Sandusky and finally south to Dayton. It has had several delays and reroutings due to bridges being washed out. I understand while it had to sit for eight hours waiting for bridge repair at West Liberty, farmers from the surrounding country- side brought in 175 wagonfuls of foodstuffs to be loaded aboard and brought here for distribution. This train brought one car of water, one car of medical supplies, two of food, one of bunks and seventy men. An addi- tional two trains of relief materials are still to be sent to us from New York.

"Other communities are similarly going to great lengths to send help in many forms — cash money, food, medicines, manpower. But the rebuilding of Dayton will take time and effort and it will cost a very great deal. We must have all the aid possible. It is my feeling that the federal government should take strong measures in this direction."

To the rear of the room Secretary of War Garrison got to his feet. "Mr. Chairman," he said, "President Wilson is well advised of the situation here and is doing all in his power as chief executive to rush this city the aid it needs. In fact," he added wryly, "you will probably re- ceive more than you actually need, at least where mate- rial supplies are concerned. While your situation here is certainly very bad, it is not by any means as serious as the news media reported it to be. Nevertheless, it is still grave, and substantial aid is forthcoming."

"We must also," Patterson went on without comment when Garrison sat down, "begin immediately to think of Dayton's future. Steps must be taken to see that such a catastrophe may not happen to this city again. The Citizen's Relief Committee will meet immediately after this session ends to discuss ways and means by which this might be accomplished without delay."

The meeting continued in greater detail with various officials commenting about the extent of the flood, work that had to be done and yet remained to do in order to return Dayton to some degree of normalcy.

Finally Secretary of War Garrison asked how many of the dead had been found and Montgomery County Coroner John W. McKemy stood up. "The final total will not, I'm happy to say, come anywhere near the early estimates of many thousands. In fact," he said flatly, "there will be an exceptionally *low* death toll considering what we've been through. This has been due in great measure to Mr. Patterson and his quick action out here at NCR. Without his boats, his men and the services he provided, the total number of dead would undoubtedly have been much higher. There have been 72 bodies located since the waters receded yesterday morning, taking the total of dead recovered at this point to approximately 120. Despite the clouded factor of numerous cases where bodies have been reported as recovered and buried without official report being made, I think I can safely say now that the total death toll will probably not be over 300. I find this highly remarkable when it is considered what this city has withstood, not only from high waters but from the devastating fires which struck at numerous places in the city and could not be controlled."

General Wood nodded and faced the assemblage as McKemy seated himself. "Gentlemen," he said, "I think we have covered with reasonable thoroughness all aspects of the situation for the moment and there is much work to be done. Mr. Patterson's committee will meet immediately following our adjournment here, and I would like to hold a meeting of my own of all the military officers, including Mr. Garrison and General Wood — the other one, that is," he added and the group laughed as he indicated General Leonard Wood, chief of staff of the United States Army, who had come to Dayton with the War Secretary and now sat beside him. "Well then, does anyone have anything further to add before this meeting is officially closed?"

Patterson stood up. "I would like to say just this. On behalf of the city of Dayton, I want to thank all of you gentlemen who have come to Dayton from great distances to help. It is with your help that Dayton will become an even bigger and better city. The press and public is, of course, anxious to know what will be done. By this afternoon sometime, I hope the Citizen's Relief Committee will have come up with an answer. There will be a meeting for the press tomorrow noon, at which time plans will be publicly outlined. In addition to the press I would like to have in attendance, if possible, all of us gathered here, as well as those in charge of relief posts and divisions, sanitary officials and military officers who will remain on duty here. Thank you, gentlemen."

Sunday

✱ 11 A.M.

THE RELIEF line stretched for two blocks along K Street to the side door of the National Cash Register Company, and the suffering reflected on the faces of refugees waiting for bread and soup was tragic.

A gangling, scraggly-whiskered laborer with rotten teeth and a sour breath scratched himself under the arm of his filthy coveralls and complained bitterly to the man behind him in the line.

"It's them damn' millionaires what caused all this!" he said passionately. "They got all th' money an' could'a prevented this from happenin', but they ain't about to give up none of that money."

"That so?" asked the other man who was a short, rather bland-looking older individual. He, too, wore coveralls of the type given out at NCR.

"Hell, yes, it's so! You k'n bet you won't find them lousy buggers wantin' food or clothes or losin' anything they got. No siree! By God, it's them millionaires'll make a fortune on this flood an' it'll be at our expense."

"Really?" The older man looked interested. "How so?"

"Never mind how," the first man said vaguely. "Jes' take my word for it, they'll make out. They allus do."

When they reached the head of the line, each of the men received three small loaves of bread and a sack of potatoes. The whiskered man slapped his companion on the shoulder and grinned. "Ummm," he said, "thought I'd never see fresh bread again. Looks like you could use a little, too."

"I have been a little hungry," the other admitted.

"Well, reckon I'd better get on home. Wife'll be wonderin' where I am. Suspiciousest woman you ever seen!"

"Your home is in pretty good shape?"

"Oh, yeah, water dint even touch it. We made out pretty good, 'cept we ain't been able to get no bread nowhere till now. You lose much in the flood?"

"Yes," the older man said softly, "just about everything."

"Say, that's too bad. I'd invite you to come eat with us but my brother an' his family's there sponging on us already an' we ain't got more'n just enough for us."

"That's generous of you, but I'll be all right. Good-by."

"Mebbe I'll see you again some time. My name's Roal Ruppert. What's yours?"

"Barney. Eugene J. Barney," the older man said simply, turning away.

Ruppert didn't recognize the name, but that wasn't surprising, since he never read the papers. He might have been a little surprised had he realized that Barney had, two days before the flood, donated $25,000 to the

Dayton YMCA. He was also a millionaire many times over . . . who had lost virtually everything during this past week.

✳ **NOON**
SUNDAY

General George H. Wood stood on the stage and raised his hands for quiet. The rumble of voices from over a thousand throats gradually quieted. In the audience were military authorities, representatives from the capitals of nation and state, news reporters from all over the country, Red Cross and health officials, rescue and relief officials of the city and every available civic leader of Dayton.

"This meeting," Wood announced, "has been called by Mr. Patterson to explain what has already been done in Dayton, what is being done now and what remains to be done. Mr. Patterson will be delayed for a short time and so I will ask our United States Secretary of War, Mr. Garrison, who is here as direct representative of President Woodrow Wilson, to make a few comments. Mr. Secretary?"

Garrison, amidst heavy applause, climbed to the podium. "While you have undergone a terrible ordeal here," he began when silence fell again, "you seem to have the situation remarkably well in hand. In fact, where immediate emergency work was concerned, you have done everything here by yourselves in an exceptional manner. We can do nothing more in this respect than you have already done.

[326]

"The people of this NCR community — as that is what this company has become during this week — have done wonderful work in the way of lending a hand to the people of Dayton and are entitled to great credit. It seems to me that you are getting an abundance of food supplies, your stricken people are being well care for and the work has been remarkably well systematized. We, from the government, propose to give you adequate sanitary protection and afford all the help possible for the well being of the citizens of this city and community. We have permission from Governor Cox to proceed with our plans and we propose to do so without delay.

"The city will be divided into sixteen sanitary districts with a United States expert in charge of each. With me to help in this are the men who accompanied me here — General Wood, head of the U.S. Army, Major Thomas Rhoads of the White House Corps, Surgeon General Blue of Cincinnati, Assistant Surgeon General Rucker of Washington and Surgeon Willi of Cleveland, all of whom are with the National Public Health District."

The men stood as he called their names and then sat down again as he continued. "While the early reports of the situation in this city that reached Washington were somewhat overdrawn, yet conditions are such as to demand quick and drastic action, and this doubtless will be taken. The President is greatly concerned about the conditions prevailing here and issued a special request that I wire him at the earliest possibility, giving him accurate details. I have already conformed to his wish, but have not yet had further word from him. I do anticipate, however, that he will authorize fully the help we propose here. Thank you."

He left the stage under another barrage of clapping, and General Wood called for silence. "I am informed," he said, "that Mr. Patterson will be here momentarily, and in the meanwhile perhaps I can explain about the martial law in effect here and —"

"General Wood, if you please!"

Feet shuffled and heads craned to see the man who had jumped from his seat at the rear and waved his hand frantically to be recognized. The general, bridling a little at being interrupted in this manner, said stiffly, "Your name, please?"

"Breen. Frank Breen. I'm city solicitor of Dayton. I'd like to complain about this martial law thing you've established here. I've been having all kinds of clashes with soldiers over martial law and I tell you, things have come to a funny pass when a city official of such a municipality as Dayton must be continually pulling out some sort of cardboard to allow him to go where he wishes. The city officials are supreme in every city in the State of Ohio and I can prove it! These soldiers are no more than state policemen and should be governed and govern themselves accordingly. If it were not so serious it would be comical to see how Service Director Charley Hoglen and myself have been tossed about like rag babies by the soldiers since the flood. I am getting tired of it and am going to take the action necessary to stop it. If I ever get the opportunity to do so, I shall tell Governor Cox a few things which have not been brought to his attention. I shall explain to him the proper functions of his soldiery!"

He finished on a loud note and stood there for a moment as if awaiting applause. When only a stunned silence was there he muttered something unintelligible and sat down.

"I am sure," said General Wood coldly, "that Governor Cox would be most interested in learning whatever it is you feel has not been brought to his attention regarding martial law. Until that time, however, by order of the governor, Dayton will remain under martial law, which has the power to eclipse municipal law and which is answerable only to the governor himself.

"What I was intending to say when Mr. Breen gave us his comment is that in times of great municipal disaster it becomes necessary, however distasteful, to place a city under martial law until such time as conditions more nearly approach a normal state. It is for protection rather than hindrance of the citizens that this is done. How long this martial law will remain in effect in Dayton we cannot accurately judge at this time, but we hope it will not be necessary for longer than a month. In the meanwhile, anyone with a justifiable reason for moving about the city will be given — if he has not already received one — a pass. He must, however, show this pass for identification if requested to do so by any military authority, whether it be a private on guard duty or a commanding officer directing operations." He paused and looked to the rear of the hall, then smiled. "And now," he said, "here is your chairman of the Citizens Relief Committee, Mr. John H. Patterson."

[329]

A great applause filled the air as Patterson entered at the rear of the auditorium and it grew as he walked to the stage. Before long the entire assemblage was on its feet and it was many minutes before the clapping died down and they resumed their seats.

The industrialist abruptly swept out his arm to indicate the entire city. *"This must never happen again!"* he said, and instantly the hall was filled with roaring applause again, intermingled with cheers.

"We here in Dayton," Patterson said at length, "have lived through a nightmare of fire and water. We have witnessed a segment of hell right here in Dayton, and we must not let it occur again if Dayton is to live and grow.

"We are already planning for a greater, a richer, a more beautiful and safer Dayton. I wish to lay emphasis upon the fact that Dayton will be made safe. *I pledge my word on that!* I have already contracted with engineering experts to go over the situation and begin making plans for a Dayton that will be absolutely safe and secure. In spite of the loss of life, the ruin and desolation everywhere apparent, the calamity may prove a blessing in disguise. It has brought us all to the need of close cooperation and civic enthusiasm and all of us will work now for a greater city.

"The entire situation," he continued, "is now completely in hand, thanks to the prompt action of President Wilson in sending Secretary of War Garrison, General Wood, Colonel Rupert Blue and his associates to us. The work of cleaning up the city is now progressing satisfactorily. Every available truck and horse drawn dray is being impressed into work, as are many hundreds of men. One of our first tasks must be the removal of almost fifteen hundred dead horses from our streets, along with three thousand or more other dead animals. The general clean-up will be very difficult and will take much time. Broken glass is everywhere, mud is feet deep in most areas and all sorts of fixtures and merchandise are piled on sidewalks. Perhaps a thousand homes have been destroyed and well over two thousand more will have to be razed and new ones built.

"Upon the arrival here of the Secretary of War, Governor Cox promptly advised him by telephone to use his own judgment in appointing a chief sanitary officer. Major Thomas L. Rhoads, who was appointed to this position, has divided the city into sixteen districts, each in charge of a district sanitary officer, and each sanitary officer has his own staff selected from among local physicians and volunteer physicians from other cities. More than three hundred doctors — thirty-five from other cities — will be working under the direction of Major Rhoads. His instructions in brief form have been sent broadcast over the city, giving definite directions to the inhabitants for the safeguarding of health. A few of the points I would reiterate here because of their importance.

"Dr. A. H. Lane," he continued, "one of our local health officers, has told me there are exceptionally few contagious diseases in the city. This has in part been aided by the cold weather, which has helped to retard decomposition. There are nine cases of diphtheria in isolation in Miami Valley Hospital. Seven of these are people who were marooned in a home with a person who had just contracted the disease. There is no danger of uncontrolled spreading of contagion from this source. On the other hand, however, there is still a severe water shortage, and contagion with effects as bad as the flood itself can quite easily break out if all city water is not boiled.

"The sewer and water system is rapidly being reopened and will probably be in working order soon. But until then all garbage and sewage must be buried. The telephone and telegraph companies have ben rushing operations into the city, but have so far been utterly unable to answer all telegrams asking for information. This has been particularly hard on relatives of Dayton people, but to relieve the anxiety as far as possible, I have been told today by Coroner John McKemy that he is now entirely confident that the final death toll will be in the vicinity of two hundred individuals."

There was more applause at this and in the press section, reporters scribbled furiously. This was their first truly official statement received since their arrival, and they made the most of it.

"There are many injured people, of course," Patterson went on, "who are receiving excellent treatment from our medical men. Unfortunately, there are also thirty-seven people who have lost their minds — let us hope only temporarily — and have been removed to Dayton State Hospital.

"We will," he added, "have twenty to forty thousand

people to feed for two weeks and we will have twenty thousand people who will have to be fed and clothed for several weeks and eventually financed in order that they may reestablish their housekeeping.

"A loan committee of twenty-two local building association directorates and banking institutions has just finished meeting — the reason why," he added as an aside, "I was late for this meeting — and discussed the matter of rebuilding; what it will cost and how the citizens of Dayton will be able to afford it. The meeting was held in the office of Dayton treasurer W. F. Bippus to determine ways and means of obtaining a loan of $40 million from the national government for this purpose, since there is no surplus in the county.

"It was proposed that an effort be made to have Congress set aside this $40 million under control of a national board appointed by President Wilson and that this amount be drawn upon by banks, trust companies and building associations at such times and in such amounts as they may see fit and that security may therefore be furnished of such character as the board may demand, and as such to be considered necessary to make the government absolutely safe.

"There were," he added, "many details discussed, but briefly, it was advised that the rate of interest be fixed at four per cent for the first five years, with an increasing rate of one-half of one per cent additional each year until the entire government loan shall have been repaid. To guarantee the national government against loss, it was suggested that Dayton offer $60 million of banking and building association security as collateral for the loan. In this way the government would be risking nothing and Dayton at the same time would be restored to new life and her former prosperity. I might add that all those present at the meeting agreed as to the feasibility of the proposition, and this is the course of action that will doubtless be pursued.

"Now then, where actual relief is concerned, we are in fairly good shape here. We have plenty of clothing, but could use more blankets, underwear, shoes and stoves. Whatever food is going to be sent here should be imperishable. The suffering, generally, throughout the city has been very much relieved and with the organization we have now, everyone will soon be properly clothed and housed. There are enough doctors in the city to take care of all medical work. We are also fairly well supplied with nurses, although nurses competent to act as instructors would be welcomed. The city has suffered a greater financial loss by the flood than it would have had a fire swept the same area, as there was practically no insurance carried on the city against floods.

"As you have no doubt already experienced, while the city is under martial law it will be necessary for each of us to show passes to military authorities when requested."

There was a great burst of laughter as this, which only increased at the puzzlement in Patterson's face. "I didn't realize," he said drily as it died away, "that I was so effective a humorist." There was more laughter at that, but he raised his hand and went on. "Everyone here and anyone else legitimately requiring a pass will be issued one by General Wood, Captain Cyrus Mead, Lieutenant Clark, any of the zone commissioners or myself.

"The purpose of such passes, of course, is to keep our city free not only from marauders who might loot and rob, but equally to keep out sight-seers who have come to see what shape our city is in and would only complicate clean-up operations.

"It might interest you to know," he added, "that over fifty thousand sightseers have come to Dayton in the past three days. They have come by car, motorcycle, carriage, horseback, on foot and even by railroad handcars. They bring their lunches and plan to spend the day wandering about just looking. Most of these have been repulsed at the city limits and sent their way, but altogether too many are slipping in, and this is the principal reason for our need of official passes.

"Those who get into the city," he said grimly, "will be shown little sympathy or courtesy. These people will be impressed into work details and forced to help with the general clean-up at bayonet point if necessary. It would be well," he said, staring at the press section, "if the reporters here assembled would print in their papers that drones will not be tolerated in Dayton. Everyone will work. Those men carrying a camera on one arm and a female on the other are evidently not intending to work and will be questioned."

He continued, ignoring the titter that rippled through the newsmen. "We hope to import five thousand men to help with the clean-up, and we hope to follow the good example set seven years ago by San Franciscans in rebuilding their city after the earthquake.

"The National Cash Register Company," he said, "will pay all its employees full wages during the time they are off work helping with relief and reconstruction. It is hoped that other firms and businesses might do the same to help pay these people something for the great amount of work they have done and sacrifice they have made this past week.

"There remains one last thing for me to announce here." For the first time a very broad smile brightened his features. "The Citizen's Relief Committee yesterday met for long hours to discuss what is ahead in Dayton's future. I said when I came in here today that this must not happen again.

"We are recommending that a Flood Prevention Committee be established and that a fund-raising campaign be inaugurated to raise the sum of $2 million in public subscription from the citizens of Dayton — from these same people still reeling under the loss of hundreds of millions of dollars. The $2 million would not be enough to construct any adequate system of flood prevention for Dayton, but it would be a start in that direction. If we can show the United States government that we are ready and willing to help ourselves before asking for federal aid, perhaps such aid in the completion of the job will be more readily forthcoming. For this campaign the city will be divided into twenty-five districts, each with a captain and ten assistants. No pledges will be announced until May 26, but I feel confident the people of Dayton can do it.

"Dayton, gentlemen," he concluded softly, "*will* do it!"

* 7 P.M.
SUNDAY

For the first time since the beginning of the flood, electric lights came on again in some sections of Dayton. They were the forerunners of a bright future for the city.

Epilogue

FOR MORE than a month the gigantic, three-story cash register erected on the courthouse lawn at Third and Main Streets had been a center of attraction, and today, the final day of the great campaign — the campaign declared by many to be impossible and unreasonable and insane — a huge crowd began assembling in the late morning hours to watch the totals rung up.

The city streets were clean, many newly paved. Shop fronts were freshly painted and glassed and the debris of razed buildings cleared away. Each car that came in sight carried more people who were disgorged in front of that great machine.

At 11:45 A.M. the bell of the register rang and the word WAIT appeared. Then, at noon exactly, the figure of $122,000 came up, and there was a deep, disappointed murmur from the crowd. After this, however, the total changed every ten or fifteen minutes. At 1 P.M. it rang up $392,000; an hour later, $481,000. It was now at about

[338]

the figure most had expected would probably be collected, and a growing excitement gripped the crowd.

At 5:20 P.M. the figure jumped from $719,400 to $1,590,000, and there was prolonged cheering and applause. Still the total kept rising, and now it seemed that just possibly the goal might be reached. At 7:30 P.M. $1,662,000 was rung up, followed almost immediately by $1,701,000. At 8 P.M. the register showed $1,750,000.

Now a band had assembled on the courthouse steps and blared out a stirring march. At 8:05 P.M. the bell rang again, and the figure jumped to $1,900,000. The music stopped, and it suddenly seemed as if the entire city was holding its breath.

Exactly five minutes later a great spotlight from the Conover Building diagonally across the street threw the cash register into brilliant relief, the bell rang, and the figure came into view.

$2,000,000!

It was a thrilling moment. No city of Dayton's size had ever done so tremendous a thing. There was wildly enthusiastic cheering which gradually evolved into a chanting cry for "Patterson! Patterson! We want Patterson!" It became a roaring demand which lapsed into silence only when the NCR president himself took a stance in front of the gigantic cash register.

"In this most memorable action upon the part of our people in raising the fund," Patterson said, "I have been struck most forcefully not by the generosity of those wealthy ones who have the money to give, but by the ready response by the rank and file, themselves in need, perhaps, but still willing to aid the city in this great enterprise. In other words, it is the widow's mite which has appealed to me the strongest."

It was characteristic of Patterson that he made no mention of the fact that he and the NCR Company gave a total of about one-third of the entire amount collected — and this did not include the relief work of the company, amounting to more than $1 million. True to form as always, Patterson calmly charged this relief work as an operating expenditure of the company.

"The new Dayton spirit," Patterson continued to the eagerly listening crowd, "was born at the flood, and Dayton citizens are beginning to recognize at last that the affairs of the city are their own affairs. The advent of the flood has, of course, resulted in enormous material loss to the people, but it has also brought tremendous gain in the shape of new life, new vigor, new soul. It has brought the people together as they have never been before. It has brought all classes into sympathy with one another and has caused team play amongst the citizens of Dayton for the first time in this generation. Each man worked as if the whole thing depended on him alone.

"This disaster," he concluded, "was a serious loss to Dayton, but if we continue to show the spirit we are now showing, it will have been, in time, on the whole, of great benefit to Dayton. I have heard with the keenest satisfaction from Mr. Arthur E. Morgan, probably the most capable engineer on this subject in the world, that the problem of flood prevention for Dayton is one that can be solved and *will* be solved in the near future."

John H. Patterson was right. In the subsequent months and years, the Miami Conservancy District was formed, special legislation was finally secured through the state assembly and five large dams were built in the Miami Valley in a water control project second only to the Panama Canal.

Since that time of terror in 1913, western Ohio has never again sustained as much rainfall as it did during those tragic few days that March, but the Miami Conservancy Dams have nevertheless proven well their value.

On over six hundred separate occasions since they were completed in 1922, they have prevented flooding — from slight to highly serious — in Dayton.

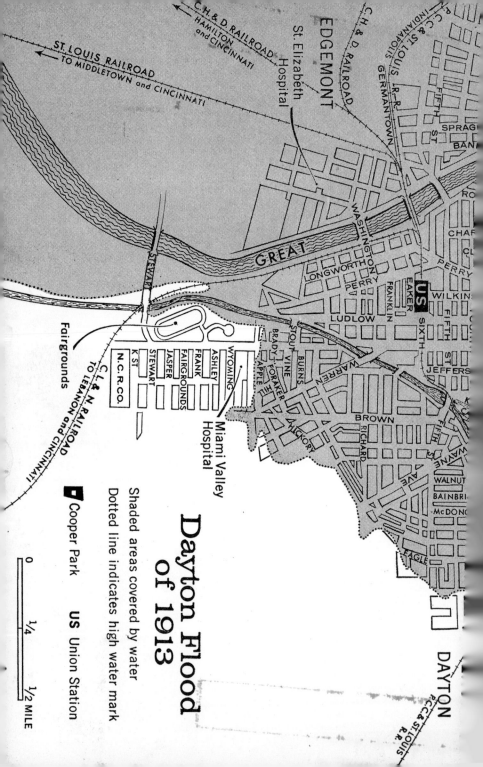

Dayton Flood
of 1913

Shaded areas covered by water
Dotted line indicates high water mark

■ Cooper Park

US Union Station

0   1/4   1/2 MILE

C.H. & D. RAILROAD
HAMILTON
and CINCINNATI

ST. LOUIS RAILROAD
TO MIDDLETOWN and CINCINNATI

St. Elizabeth Hospital

EDGEMONT

C.H. & D. RAILROAD

CC. & ST. LOUIS JR. R.
INDIANAPOLIS

CC. & ST. LOUIS JR. R.
GERMANTOWN

SPRAG
BAN
RO
CHAR
CL
PERRY
WILKIN
FIFTH
SIXTH
JEFFERS

WASHINGTON
PERRY
LONGWORTH
PERRY
FRANKLIN
LUDLOW
EAKER
US

GREAT

STEWART

Fairgrounds

C. L. & N. RAILROAD
TO LEBANON and CINCINNATI

N.C.R. CO.
K ST
STEWART
JASPER
FAIRGROUNDS
FRANK
ASHLEY
WYOMING

Miami Valley Hospital

STOUT
VINE
BRADY
FORAKER
APPLE
BURNS
HICKORY
WARREN
BROWN
RICHARD

WAYNE
AVE
WALNUT
BAINBRI
McDON

EAGLE

DAYTON

PC.C.A STLOUIS
R.R.